CALLED
FOR SUCH A
TIME AS THIS

—— THE ——

ACCOUNT OF A FRONTLINE
COVID-19 NURSE

ESTHER OSEMWEGIE

Foreword by Dr Chinyelu Menakaya

It is a pleasure to know
you. You are making such a
difference in your job and your
environment. Thank you for
being you. You are called for
such a time as this. Esomyo 20/10/20

© 2020 Esther Osemwegie
UK Copyright Service
Oxfordshire, United Kingdom
RN 284736437

Cover design & layout by David Springer 2020

Dedication

This book is dedicated to my fellow health care professionals; to our comrades and partners who laid down their lives in the field of different hospitals and care settings during this pandemic but couldn't make it to the end. Alas! your lives were snatched wickedly and quickly by the treacherous coronavirus while you were trying to save others from the deadly disease.

I may not know your names, but God knows who you are. Your labour of love will never be forgotten in the hearts of many. My prayer is that God Almighty will keep and watch over your loved ones who were left behind. May He fill the vacuum created by your absence with His love and tender mercies. Although you are no longer here with us, your legacy and your sacrifice of love will live on and on.

Sleep on, champs. You were simply the best.

I am so proud of you.

With love,

Esther

TABLE OF CONTENTS

Acknowledgements

First of all, I would like to give thanks to God for His divine protection over us during this pandemic. Thank you, father God for the wisdom and inspiration to write this book. Thank you for your divine provision and for making a way where there seems to be no way.

My sincere thanks to my husband, Victor Moses A. Osemwegie, for allowing me to be me and giving me space and time to pursue the things that I'm passionate about. Darling, thanks for putting up with my tears and wet hair on the pillow after washing my hair at midnight after work—being too tired to use the dryer but sneaking into bed anyway.

Thanks to my lovely three heroes – Elvis, Evans, and Marvin (my three sons) – for caring, listening, and encouraging while I was writing this book and in so many things in my life. Thanks to my lovely daughter Chi-Chi for giving me rides to and from work; for being my prayer partner and my confidant.

To my two daughters-in-law, Agnese and Sarah, for checking on me. Thanks to our lovely Joshua Nwatar for his prayer and encouragement. To my beautiful and handsome grandchildren Jerimiah, Kairos, Kressida, Peninah, Ketrina and Noah for the joy they brought to my life.

Special thanks to my wonderful spiritual leader, teacher, and mentor Dr Bishop Wayne Malcolm for his prayers, leadership, teaching, training, and preaching of the word of God that has been our guide during this pandemic. Bishop, your love and emphasis for Queen Esther has always inspired me as you brought the meaning of that name alive; it has been my dream to just tap into her role in the service of saving lives – "my people" – as per your training, the Mordecai Coaching. The truth is that my people were still invisible in my human eye until the light bulb or the "aha" moment. I know that my status has not reflected on your intellectual investment in me yet, but I can assure you that I am still a work in progress. I salute you, sir.

Thanks to David Springer for his skill in the art of Graphic design. David, you were able to read my mind through your skill to bring my story to life through this book cover. Thanks for your labour of love.

Thanks to my entire family, both in England and abroad, for their prayers.

Special thanks to Mr Isaac Carter and the mentors of the Entrepreneur Club, Every little help has been an important step for me. I am very grateful.

Special thanks to Claudine Reid for her leadership in women's ministry and navigating life series. Your coaching and mentorship through the series have been a source of strength, motivation and inspiration to me. I am truly grateful.

Thanks to my friends Kim Bacchus, Sandra Mighty, and Theresa Clarke-Livingston for their support and encouragement. Thanks to all ICC members for their prayers for me during this pandemic.

I am indeed grateful to God for both the good times and the times that are not so good in my life, for they have all come together to make me who I am becoming.

Foreword

Caring for others, touching lives, and putting your life on the frontline, even at a point when uncertainty masks the air you breathe, is a calling. It is a calling to serve. It is a calling to continue to smile even though you know that the outcome may be fatal. It is not a fairy tale—it's a good description of many of the most amazing people I have encountered inside the walls of the hospital. They wear crisp outfits, they smile even when fear grips them, they hold hands of strangers that they just met and they sit with the "afraid dying"— listening, offering succour and helping them cross over to the land away from this world or leading them back through paths of healing.

Great health workers care for patients every day. Nurses care for patients above themselves. This was the experience I encountered on the first day I met Mrs. Esther Osemwegie. From her first words to me as a surgeon, I knew my patients were in the safest hands. She remains an amazing nurse.

When the wind of the COVID-19 pandemic gripped the world to a standstill, Esther, a nurse of over 16 years' experience, faced a new type of nursing. Despite the difficulty of the pandemic and the "new" way of caring for the sick, without the support of their immediate families, she rose to the core-giving philosophy of "patient first above herself", despite the fear that was all around her. She sacrificed the "panic of the family" as she offered her services on the frontline and the "voice of worry" from within to work with COVID-19 patients.

"Called for such a time as this....." captures that philosophy of caring above one's personal needs and against all odds. It recounts that nursing isn't a parable or fiction or a dream but a reality. This book follows Esther's encounters with real patients during a pandemic that brought the world to a stop. She recounts her wins, her fears, her courage, and, most importantly, the experiences her patients shared with her as they fought a battle with a disease the world continues to try to understand. She was called to care for the dying and critically ill at this time, that time and still now.

Despite her risk factors, she rose under the wings of extensive nursing experience and her dedication to duty and imprinted her mark to save patients and to serve the country. She reminds us of the sacrifices workers on the frontline make on a day-to-day basis for the love of their patients. Despite her challenges and her fears, she offers help, succour, and bring peace to her patients throughout the pandemic.

"Called for such a time as this..... " helps you understand the beauty of the profession in the frontline.

Dr Chichi Menakaya
Surgeon, London, UK

Preface

A BRIEF WORD FROM ESTHER OSEMWEGIE

We are entering into a new normal. What we think of as normal in our life is changing before our eyes. All those things that we thought we couldn't do without are almost vanishing before our eyes. Who could have told us, especially those of us living in the Western world, that there would be a time we would not be allowed to visit our GP practice, call the ambulance services over things that are not deemed as serious, or go to the Accident and Emergency over the least medical conditions that we could have dealt with at home? Moreover, how would we have been able to fathom that we would not be able to gather at will in public places, churches, and faith centres, as they have moved their services online? How would we have foreseen that we would be unable to give befitting send-offs to our loved ones, that airports would be closed and airplanes grounded, the schools closed, and every part of our lives affected, with industries, financial institutions, and big businesses on their knees as a result of the outbreak of the virus? At the time of this writing, the source is still a mystery to the world – still a secret – and some can only guess at it. It is an unprecedented time, but it will come to pass.

In this book, I have given some raw accounts of my experience while caring for COVID-19 patients. The dates of certain events during the pandemic are included for the simple reason that in generations to come, those coming after us may at any time pick up this book and will be able to put times to the different events. I highlight the risk and stress that healthcare professionals, especially the nurses and doctors, were faced with daily but particularly during the pandemic.

I have included in the book my fears, anxiety, prayers, strengths, and vulnerabilities during this unprecedented time. Included also is the meaning behind the name of the book. The name and the character behind the name have been an inspiration to me.

It is important to know that, for confidentiality, none of the initials used in the book are the initials of the subjects. The names of the hospitals were intentionally excluded, and the names of the wards are not real.

I do appreciate the clapping of hands for healthcare workers. However, I am looking up to the political parties, the activists or other people of influence that we do the right thing and call for a pay increase for NHS staff on all levels, including those that worked for the NHS through the agencies, care homes, and home carers. I do not mean a pay increase of 2% over 6 years that, at the end of the day, cannot buy them a sandwich.

*"Hello Sir,
I am Esther.
I'm one of the nurses that
have been looking after you."*

*The COVID-19 survivor broke
down in the hospital wheelchair
before the porter and wept.
"I'm sorry sir, what have I done?"
I asked.
"You are the first face that I've
seen for over a month since my
admission, until today,"
he said.*

CHAPTER 1

FACING MY FEAR

FACING MY FEAR

I t was a very cold Monday morning in London. Most of the trains from Waterloo East train station were delayed, so I was late to work by three minutes. No point going to the handover room, where we meet at the beginning of a shift to coordinate patient care, as the matron would have already shut the door. I had no choice but to wait by the ward coordinator's desk. I had already spoken to the manager and the matron about my commute through London Bridge station; how the constant delay of the trains affects my connecting train to work.

This particular morning, things looked different in the ward, even though the feeling was difficult to pinpoint. As I stood thinking about what might have changed, I began to notice that colour-coded tapes were marking the floors. In front of the bays were some unusual bins that were not normally there, and the doors that were usually open were closed. The ward was noticeably quiet except for the noise of nebulizers. *There are more people than ever using nebulizers this morning,* I thought. The night nurses had yellow aprons, masks, caps, and scrubs. I decided to investigate.

As I was about to open one of the doors, I felt someone pulling my tunic from the back.

"Sister, please stop, do not go in there!" pleaded a co-worker.

"Why not?" I asked.

"Were you not in the handover room?" she faintly asked. I said that I wasn't, and I needed to find out which patients I had been allocated because I was late and could not get into the handover room.

"Hold on, look at me. If you like, you can keep going, but I am not here to die."

"What on earth are you talking about?" I inquired, with my voice slightly raised and my eyes wild. "Who is it that wants to kill you?"

"I am going to call my agency now," she said, looking confused. An agency nurse is a temporarily employed nurse who works for a day or more to cover staff shortage. I needed to go for my allocation, but at the same time, I wanted to know what on earth was going on and who it was that wanted to kill her, and for what reason?

"Did the nurse in charge give you too many patients?" I asked, "All you need is to ask for help." I tried to persuade her to stay. "We will help each other; you know that the nursing job is getting harder by the day."

"Esther, look around yourself," she said, "It isn't just about the hard work. The ward is full of coronavirus patients."

"Sis, do you mean COVID-19?" I asked. Without knowing how to process the information, I was confused. I'm already here; I cannot go back home. That would be unprofessional. I'm already booked as part of the team; someone's life depends on my presence here today, and the team will struggle with two nurses down. With all this going through my mind, I decided to go for it. At least I have the experience, and as nurses, our job is to save lives and not to shy away from things like this, no matter how challenging they are.

I went straight to report to the nurse in charge of the shift. She handed a little bunch of keys to me, followed by a handover from the night staff who worked in the bay. We discussed the fact that COVID-19 patients are now in the hospital, even more than they are in the ward, which was something we did not envision as we bade each other farewell and good weekend wishes on Friday. She told me that the good news is that none of my patients are COVID-19 positive. This was indeed very good news, which was followed by a big thanks to God within my spirit. Later in the day, I had a few discharges. The bay was particularly busy, but this was better than having COVID-19 patients.

Just before noon, a patient whom I will refer to as Mrs BB was brought to my bay from a COVID-19 bay. She was handed over from A&E (Accident and Emergency) on admission as a possible COVID-19 patient. I am not sure of the date of her admission to the hospital; she was admitted to the same bay among the patients who were COVID-19 positive. On this Monday afternoon, the results came back negative after days of being exposed to COVID-19 positive patients. She was transferred to my non-COVID bay. She was admitted with an exacerbation of Chronic Obstructive Pulmonary Disease (COPD). This is one of the most serious lung diseases prevalent today and affects 65 million people worldwide. From moderate chronic bronchitis to severe emphysema, COPD covers a range of debilitating lung conditions that limit airflow to the lungs.

Mrs BB will be discharged this evening after review and given medications to take home. The nurse in charge had handed the information over to me. I overheard Mrs BB telling her family that her condition had not gotten better; rather, it was worse than when she was admitted and there's no way she was going home today. To be fair to her, she was coughing extensively, and her temperature was slightly high. I had never met her before, and, as such, her condition was difficult to judge. She was on oxygen and it had been confirmed that she had been on home oxygen as well. According to her, her symptoms seemed to have become worse than they were when she came in. She had told me that she would rather die in the hospital than go home and die on her own. According to her record, she lived by herself, with social service input. Although she had children, they lived far away and one of them was admitted to a hospital somewhere outside London due to respiratory problems. I went to call the doctor to review her because there was no way that I was going to send her home in that condition. If anything happened to her at home, I would be among those to be held responsible.

The nurse in charge had decided that Mrs BB had to go because she was on home oxygen and her bed had been given to another patient coming from Accident and Emergency. I called the doctor to review her case and expressed my concerns. The doctor shared my concerns too and decided that Mrs BB had to go to a respiratory ward. I was relieved by the decision made by the doctor. Even if the team had managed to discharge the patient home with the help of hospital transport, she would have come back to the hospital; it would have been a failed discharge. It is often the case that patients are not given the chance to recover before being discharged. They end up coming back to the hospital after a day or two. If the patient is not able to speak out because of their condition, before you knew it, they would go home and probably come back to the hospital the same night or the following morning. It was quite obvious that Mrs BB was anxious about the discharge and that's why she was becoming more breathless. Anxiety in patients with respiratory problems is not uncommon. Safa et al. also say that anxiety is a well-known symptom that is prevalent among chronic obstructive disease patients. It can prolong and increase the risk of hospitalization (Safa et al, 2015).

There was another 87-years-old woman, Mrs BA, who came in over the weekend after a fall. She was so sweet. She had developed a new onset of confusion but was lovely. She was refusing to eat and drink, so I had a hard time trying to get something down her. She had vomited thrice, even after antiemetics, so we had decided to keep her free from oral intake but leave her on an intravenous fluid to keep her hydrated. At 1730 hours, when I took her vital signs, her temperature was 39.2 degrees centigrade, her respirations were high, and her NEWS score, which determines a patient's degree of illness, was high. I quickly went to tell the doctor. This was followed by an ECG and other clinical interventions, among which a COVID-19 swab was included, followed by frequent observations. Mrs BA's son had called earlier on to inquire about her wellbeing. He planned to come to visit after work at 1900 hours, but his mother was not at all well.

"She is far worse than she was when she came in," he said.

"Yes sir, she is very unwell, but we are on top of things," I reassured him. "I will get the doctor to speak to you." I wanted to solace him.

The doctor had told me that she might change Mrs BA's resuscitation status, as she was still slated for resuscitation. This meant that should her heart stop beating, the doctor does not want the team to attempt to start her heart again. Even though that was what the doctor recommended, it was subject to the family's approval; until that was done, she was technically lined up for resuscitation.

Another problem I had was that Mrs BA's son was visiting. Because the patient's swab hadn't yet come back positive, I couldn't tell him not to visit. I gave him a mask and an apron to put on; he was asking me why he had to put them on. I told him that it was due to the level of infection in the ward. He suspected it was due to coronavirus! He wanted to know if his mother had the virus, as he said that she had not come to hospital initially with fever. She only had a fall. I explained to him that nothing had changed – we had only taken precautions – and that his mother had been swabbed.

"I have to leave. I will call for an update," he remarked as he left the ward. He was too upset to discuss his mother's resuscitation status. His last remark was that "his mother was brought in due to falling and God help us if she has caught COVID-19."

Studies have shown that admitting elderly people in hospital can cause a decline in their physical and mental health. Admission in hospital can also put them at risk for other infections. One cannot rule that out in Mrs BA's case, considering the number of COVID-19 patients in the ward on the day in question. The doctor had suspected that Mrs BA might have caught COVID-19 and had asked me to put on a mask. Hence, Mrs BA's son was also advised to do so too. In a way, I was happy that he left the ward rather than be infected if it turned out later on that his mother was also COVID-19 positive!

Mrs BB, meanwhile, was transferred from the COVID-19 bay and had also become so unwell that she had to be transferred to a respiratory ward where she would have input from the respiratory specialist team. *Oh, God help us. Everything is happening at once,* I said to myself. I could only hope that my elderly lady, Mrs BA, had not caught the virus. What about Mrs BB with her respiratory problems? What if she had been infected from being admitted among the patients in the COVID-19 positive bay— she would then infect others in the respiratory ward? I was aware that elderly people and those with a history of respiratory problems are at high risk. It means that two of my patients were at high risk. If Mrs BA had been infected, her son, who had just visited, the doctor and I might also be at risk! I was overwhelmed with all these thoughts. I started praying in my mind on my way home. I was now on the train at 2100 hours. It was quiet, and I started reading the Bible from my phone. Deep within me, I was praying for God to control my mind and heal my patients.

As I travelled, I found myself reflecting on the whole shift. But the more I tried not to think about it, the more I found myself thinking about it.

CHAPTER 2

WHAT IS COVID-19?

WHAT IS COVID-19?

When we first heard the BBC broadcast on our television screens about this disease called coronavirus, most of us thought that it was going to end in China. Like most things that we are oblivious about, we didn't know that it would end up right on our doorsteps within a blink of an eye; that it was coming to hurt us in one way or the other. The families that have lost their loved ones would never have thought that they would be snatched from them so quickly, in such a cruel way, and with no time to prepare them physically, spiritually or emotionally. Yesterday they were here and today they are gone, with no time to say goodbye. It happened so quickly; the sufferings, the trauma and the deaths were real. That was the cruelty of the horror movie that changed the world—the CORONAVIRUS.

COVID-19 (Coronavirus Disease-2019) is caused by coronavirus SAR-cov-2 (Severe Acute Respiratory Syndrome Coronavirus-2 (Madsbad, 2020).

Coronavirus disease-2019 (COVID-19) is the third coronavirus infection in two decades to be originally described in Asia, after Severe Respiratory Syndrome (SARS) and Middle East Respiratory Syndrome (MERS) (Morens, 2020). The origin of the virus is still unknown. However, it was speculated that it started in the Chinese city of Wuhan. At the time of this writing, the research on the origin of the virus is still inconclusive. Though there are many conspiracy theories concerning the origin and the causes of COVID-19, none of them are included in this book as there is no concrete evidence to prove or disprove them.

It's been stated that a pneumonia of unknown cause was reported in Wuhan, China. This was first reported to the World Health Organisation's office in China on 31st December 2019. The outbreak was declared a Public Health Emergency, and of international concern, on 30th January 2020. The first confirmed cases in the United Kingdom were in late January 2020.

On 13th March 2020, the World Health Organisation assessed COVID-19 and declared it a pandemic following their concern over its alarming level of spread and the severity of the infection. A pandemic, according to the World Health Organisation, is the worldwide spread of a new disease. On 11th February 2020, the World Health Organisation announced a name for the new virus coronavirus disease, COVID-19.

The British Prime Minster Boris Johnson announced lockdown measures on 23rd March 2020.

On 19th May 2020, the 73rd World Health Assembly was held virtually, and this was the first virtual assembly ever held. The delegates adopted a landmark resolution to come together to fight the COVID-19 pandemic (who.net, 2020).

At the time of this writing, the disease is reported to have spread in up to 213 countries and territories of the world; with 12,280,505 people infected by the disease and 554,566 deaths worldwide as of 9th July 2020 [data was updated at 18:25 GMT]. Evidence has shown that there are asymptomatic carriers of COVID-19 who can transmit the disease to others (Zhong et al., 2020). Most people infected with COVID-19 disease will experience a mild to moderate respiratory illness without requiring special treatment or hospitalisation. Older people, and those with underlying medical problems like cardiovascular diseases, cancer, chronic respiratory diseases and diabetes, are more likely to develop serious illness and death (NFID, 2020).

According to the World Health Organisation, the source of the spread of this virus is primarily droplets of saliva or discharge from the nose when an infected person sneezes or coughs. The incubation period is 6-8 days on average, followed by 1 to 2 weeks of symptomatic disease. However, other studies, such as Zhong et al., show that the incubation period could also be 0 to 24 days. (Zhong et al., 2020)

Hand washing and the use of alcohol-based gel are extremely important for killing the virus. The World Health Organisation also emphasises the practice of respiratory etiquette, such as coughing into a flexed elbow. Some of the symptoms include fever, dry coughs, tiredness, loss of smell and taste, sore throat, aches and pains and, in the worst case, death (Yang, X et al., 2020).

Due to the infectivity of the virus, there is an urgent need for the development of a therapy to treat patients and to control the spread. In an effort to reduce the quick spread of the virus, several nations all over the world had to put some measures in place to protect their citizens. The measures are similar from country to country. Places like schools, churches, faith centres, restaurants and shops were closed. People whose jobs could allow them to work from home were asked to do so; only key and frontline workers were allowed to go to work. The things that we are used to as humans were shut down, and social distancing and self-isolation were advised. The lockdown that was placed on facilities and people's privileges were later eased at different times by different counties as the rate of infected people and the death rate began to dwindle. At the time of this writing, there are still no vaccines or treatment for the virus, but some clinical trials are ongoing by scientists in different countries of the world.

On the 10th of January 2020 at Oxford University in the United Kingdom, a team led by Professor Sarah Gilbert, Professor Andrew Poland, Professor Teresa Lambed, Dr Shady Douglas and Professor Adrian Hill started work on designing a vaccine. At the time of this writing, a vaccine candidate has been identified and clinical trials are being carried out.

There are no treatments for COVID-19. Rather, the condition is being managed and patients with the virus are treated according to their symptoms. Some serious symptoms are shortness of breath or difficulty in breathing, chest pain or pressure, loss of speech and loss of movement.

The BBC News on 22nd April 2020 reported that Madagascar's president had launched an herbal Coronavirus "cure". The medication is called COVID-ORGANIC. The launch was carried out at the Malagasy Institute of Applied Research (IMRA) where the drug was developed. Since there was no scientific evidence to prove the effectiveness of the medication, there has been a lot of controversy over the efficacy of the drug, and even the national medical academy is concerned about the use of the drug since it has the potential of harming those who use it. The drug was marketed in bottles claiming that COVID-ORGANIC gives results in seven days. President Rajoelina said that two individuals had been cured of the disease, and he encouraged people to use it as a preventative measure. The medication was also given to school children to take. This was agreed to by Dr Charles Andrianjara, IMRA's doctor general, who stated that COVID-ORGANIC should be used for prevention. However, the World Health Organisation responded in a statement sent to BBC that they do not recommend "self-medication" with any medicine as a prevention or cure for COVID-19.

Another controversy was on Hydroxychloroquine, which was being permitted by many countries as emergency use for COVID-19 patients in hospitals. The use of the medications was recommended and prescribed by some doctors. Dr Didier Raoult in France was amongst those who recommended the drug. Donald Trump, the President of the United States, also backed the drug's being given to patients, as he claimed that he used it to prevent contracting COVID-19. The leader of the biggest and best-designed trial of the drug has stated that the drug does not work against COVID-19 and has asked that Hydroxychloroquine should not be administered to any more patients around the world. Mr. Martin Landray, the chief investigator of the recovery trial and professor of medicine and epidemiology at Oxford University, had stated that the medicine does not work on COVID-19 patients.

On 5th June 2020, Professor Peter Horby and Professor Martin Landray responded to a request from the UK Medicine and Healthcare products Regulatory Agency (MHRA). They concluded there are no beneficial effects of Hydroxychloroquine in patients that were admitted into the hospital due to COVID-19. As a result, they have decided to immediately stop the enrolment of participants to the Hydroxychloroquine arm of the recovery trial. Preliminary results were therefore released as they have important implications for patients and public health (Recovery Trial Statement, 2020).

Peter Horby, Professor of Emerging Infectious Diseases and Global Health and chief investigator for the trial, stated that although Hydroxychloroquine and Chloroquine had received a lot of attention and had been used very widely to treat COVID-19 patients in the absence of any good evidence, the recovery trial has shown that Hydroxychloroquine is not an effective treatment in patients hospitalised with COVID-19. The above statement was also followed by Martin Landray, Professor of Medicine and Epidemiology, who stated that although there has been huge speculation and uncertainty about the role of Hydroxychloroquine as a treatment for COVID-19, there has been an absence of reliable information from large randomised trials. It was therefore clear that Hydroxychloroquine does not reduce the risk of death among hospitalized patients with COVID-19. He, therefore, concluded that the result should change medical practice worldwide and demonstrated the importance of large randomised trials to inform decisions about both the efficacy and the safety of treatment (Recovery Trial Statement, 2020).

On 15th June 2020, it was reported on the news that clinical researchers were set to begin human trials of a new coronavirus vaccine developed by researchers at Imperial College, London. According to O'Hare and Wigan, the study will be the first time the vaccine has been tried in humans and will test whether it is well-tolerated and produces an effective immune response against COVID-19 (O'Hare, R. and Wigan, K., 2020).

CHAPTER 3

RISK FACTORS OF COVID-19

RISK FACTORS OF COVID-19

W hy are certain groups of people at a higher risk of getting COVID-19? I must find out by researching it, I assured myself. The findings are important to me because my phone will not stop ringing from friends and families who are curious about this pandemic. Some of them want to know about the virus because of their own medical history, and others because of their loved ones. Apart from the foregoing, as a nurse, I need an in-depth knowledge of the virus to be able to care for my patients, give advice to them and their families, and answer their questions based on available evidence. The findings and the knowledge will come to pass as I go along this journey.

GROUPS OF PEOPLE AND THEIR RISKS

There is still limited information about COVID-19 at the time of this writing. Without a doubt, in due course and as research progresses, more light will be shed onto the disease in terms of experience and knowledge. It has been documented that the groups of people who are at a higher risk of the COVID-19 are:

* People that are 65 years and above

* Those in nursing homes or long-term care facilities

* People of all ages with underlying medical conditions, particularly if not under control

* Those with chronic lung disease and/or moderate to severe asthma

* People with serious heart conditions

* People who are immune-compromised due to such issues as cancer treatment, smoking, bone marrow or organ transplantation, immune deficiencies, poorly controlled HIV or AIDS and prolonged use of corticosteroid and other immune weakening medications.

* People with severe obesity body mass index (BMI) of 40

* People with diabetes

* People with chronic kidney disease under dialysis

* People with liver disease (Centre for Disease Control and Prevention, 2019)

Back to my Mrs BB, who came in with respiratory problems and a history of COPD—she is among one of the groups of people who are said to be in a higher risk bracket of COVID-19. But why are they at risk? Chronic obstructive pulmonary disease is a type of respiratory disorder characterised by chronic and recurrent obstruction of airflow (it increases airway resistance). It is an umbrella term for chronic lung diseases. The two main conditions are chronic bronchitis and emphysema. These diseases affect parts of the lungs, and both lead to difficulty in breathing, cough and sputum production. They affect 4.5% of people in the United Kingdom.

The British Lung Foundation estimated that 1.2 million people have been diagnosed with COPD, and it is responsible for nearly 30 thousand deaths a year (Statistics.blf.org.uk/copd).

Sissons states that people with severe COPD may have a higher risk of COVID-19 complications as the disease affects the respiratory system, which means that the existing lung damage makes it more difficult for the patients' lungs to fight off the infection (Sissons, 2020). Leung et al. found that people with chronic pulmonary disease (COPD) and those that do smoke currently may have a higher level of the molecule called angiotensin-converting enzyme 11 (ACE-2) in their lungs; they therefore highlighted the importance of smoking cessation. (Leung et al., 2020). Wan et al. and Toru et al. had also reported the same findings (Wan, Y. J., et al., 2020) and (Toru, U., et al., 2015).

Mrs BA, on the other hand, is elderly; she is also at higher risk of COVID-19 due to the physiological changes associated with aging, decreased immune function and comorbidity, which expose older adults to susceptibility to the virus itself and make them more likely to suffer severely from COVID-19 disease as well as its more serious complications (www.euro.who.com-topic/health-emergencies/ virus).

CHAPTER 4

IT'S ALL CHANGED

FROM COVID-19 NEGATIVE TO COVID-19 POSITIVE

IT'S ALL CHANGED

FROM COVID-19 NEGATIVE TO COVID-19 POSITIVE

On duty the next day and still booked in the same ward, I really did not want to go back to work. I had the choice of cancelling the shift as I only worked through a nursing agency, however there seemed to be something that kept me going. Upon reporting to work, I was transferred to another ward by the nurse in charge. I was told that the ward that I had been sent to was not a COVID-19 ward. I was kind of relieved to be transferred to a COVID-free duty. When I arrived at the ward that I had been transferred to, COVID-19 was the talk of the morning before the handover. One of the nurses believed that she was very lucky to be in a ward that was COVID-19 free. She said that she had a lot of underlying health conditions that put her at a higher risk. The ward manager had advised those in the ward who thought they were at a higher risk to speak to the ward Matron. At about noon on that Tuesday, the nurse in charge asked us to transfer some patients to other wards. Some were quickly discharged back to their homes and some were discharged to their residences or nursing homes. The moving, the discharge and the admitting were so quick that within two hours the ward had taken on a different face. It's all changed from COVID negative to COVID-19 positive.

A storeroom was converted to a changing room with scrubs and masks. No one knew whether the masks we had on were the right ones or not or if we were properly protected or not. Even the nurses who were concerned about their health didn't have the time to address their concerns with their Matron because everything was happening so quickly.

The patients were both men and women of different age groups—some at risk of COVID-19 from their previous medical history and some with no previous medical history recorded in their medical assessment notes. Some were on high-flow oxygen and some were on back-to-back nebulizers. They looked so anxious; you could read from their faces that they had so many questions in their minds. Some were too breathless to make full sentences and others looked exhausted. The nurses seemed scared and anxious but were left with no choice. No one knew what was going to happen to them. We had scrubs and surgical masks but as one of the nurses said, "We were not even sure if we are protected". None of us had any formal training on how to look after COVID-19 patients or what to expect. We knew the symptoms, so we had to work according to the care plan, measuring vital signs or signs of distress from the patient. Each patient had different symptoms and often reacted differently to the virus, so not everyone was treated the same. They were all individuals and their care plans were individualised. The assessment was difficult, as they were breathless, and we had to give them time to speak from behind oxygen masks. We had to call on some families to give us detailed information about their loved ones in our care. It is important to get all of the patient's next of kin contact numbers, should anything happen. We don't pray for the worst to happen, but as professionals, we have to be real. These people are in a hospital and, to crown it all, they are COVID-19 positive.

We had to do a standing and lying blood pressure for one of the patients as he could no longer stand without assistance. It took a while for the cuff to inflate and deflate, meaning I would be standing face to face with the patient. *He is COVID-19 positive; what about my safety?* I was speaking to myself. I had to double mask myself, and with the help of another nurse, lying and standing blood pressure was finally done. We were happy that we were able to do it. You cannot deny a patient's procedure because of the risk to yourself. That's why the PPEs are there. There is no way that we can justify not carrying out any procedure that is requested on a patient by the doctors, as this could cost the individual's life.

Supper was served but was hardly eaten by any of the patients. COVID-19 is so terrible that not only did the patients not eat their food, the sight of the food was making them throw up. From one patient vomiting to the other, a lot of antiemetic treatments were going on; we were changing sheets and patient's clothing from one patient to the next. The teamwork was fantastic, we were there for each other for the benefit of the patients. I remember one patient in particular that was so bad that he vomited into his oxygen face mask, on his table, phone, clothes and bedding. We were so scared, we thought he was going to aspirate on his vomit. The doctor had written him up for more intravenous fluid to hydrate him and improve his blood pressure. He had lost so much fluid from vomiting that his blood pressure had become dangerously low. Although we tried to keep ourselves safe as much as possible, we were very close to the patient as he was so unwell. Even though he was extremely sick, he was still able to thank us for his care. When a patient is unwell and still manages to say the magic words to me, it just kind of pushes my adrenaline higher.

One cannot fail to see that the team was now ready for the challenge; to help the patients and care for them as diligently as humanly possible. For me, the fear is no longer as bad, the patients are real patients and humans, COVID-19 is what it is. The patients need to be cared for. The team seems to have become too busy to entertain any form of fear but to concentrate on saving lives. The patient's families were calling—we could easily notice the fear in their voices, and we could sense their emotions.

There was a particular case where a young man was supposed to be travelling out of the UK with his long-time fiancée for their wedding the following weekend. He was worried about his health as well as the money they had paid out for their wedding preparation. "We have been living together for 5 years," he told me as he struggled to breathe, "It's taken us more than 6 years together to save for the big day". He went on, "Now see where we find ourselves. I feel so bad, especially for my fiancée." He told me that she is so beautiful, and she had everything a man can ever dream of in a woman. I didn't know what to say, other than to reassure him and advise him to concentrate on his health and get better. I encouraged him in a calm voice to keep his masks on, and that all will be well. His fiancée had also called the ward to speak to the doctors and the nurse looking after her fiancé. They were both really worried about his health outcome and their forthcoming wedding. "Nurse, please tell me the truth. Between us both, is he going to die?" "I am sure he will pull through." I assured her, "Please be positive and look after yourself." There wasn't much to tell her because it was really my first time looking after a COVID-19 patient. Looking back now, I am very sure that he made it.

My agency had promised me that they were going to make sure that I was not sent to any COVID-19 ward. Here I am, so very unprepared to handle this, clinically, physically, mentally, emotionally and spiritually. I was so unprepared as I stood by the computer trying to complete my clinical evaluations with all these thoughts going through my head. It was almost time to hand over to the night staff, so I tried to put myself together to carry out the task. Some of the night nurses were just shocked; some of them that had friends in the ward had been informed of the changes but were still unprepared. Before the end of the shift, the patients appeared to be stable, with their high-flow oxygen and nebulizers singing choruses.

CHAPTER 5

THE BATTLE IN MY MIND

THE BATTLE IN MY MIND

The following day was my day off. I had not slept throughout the night as my mind was all over the place, in and out of decisions, and I couldn't make up my mind about what to do next. I remained unsure about my career now, and, after the experience of the previous day, even more unsure of where we as people are going. The phone call from a patient's loved one just broke my heart, and I began to reflect on things. She had asked me if her fiancé was going to die. How I am supposed to know? Only God knows. From my own clinical judgement and his vital signs during that day, I felt he was not going to die. On the other hand, he came in with COVID-19, very breathless, and that was my first time nursing a COVID-

19 patient. Mrs BB and Mrs BA were not confirmed positive before the end of the shift, so I couldn't count on that experience. Therefore, it was my first time nursing a patient with the virus¬¬¬—not one patient either, to begin with, and not even two. But SIX patients at once. Let me tell you, Wow! That was heavy.

NO TRUE SOLDIER HIDES FROM WAR

As my mind was wandering in the valley of indecision, my phone rang. The phone call was from my agency consultant. He told me that it had been reported that most of the wards are likely to be COVID-19 positive for now. He expressed his fears and concerns about the situation and asked if I could have this period off as he deemed the situation too risky. I told him that I am a nurse and I will continue to play my role to save lives. He was surprised, as some of the nurses were by then self-isolating. True soldiers do not run away or hide at the time of war. If I stay away, I will let myself and the profession down. Life is full of risks, I told him, but I'd rather join the thousands of nurses who have taken the same risk to go to war against COVID-19, and that every one of us has a role to play in the war against this disease.

"Aren't you scared?" he asked. "Please Esther, I don't want anything to happen to you." I told him that God is watching over me. At the end of the conversation, I went to pray. My church members were already on a forty-day fast and prayers over the pandemic, for the nation and the world at large. I am among those fasting and praying. We are also praying against the spirit of fear. I have prayed that God might grant me strength at these trying times to remain resolute and steadfast. I need to be focused on God's word that He will take care of me. I was determined not to allow the power of fear to take the best part of me. I remember a book that said, "Feel the fear and do it anyway." (Jeffers 2017).

To be quite honest, I am sure that there are no health professionals who will be going into a COVID-19 ward without having concerns over their own safety, but when duty calls for it, one is obliged to respond. At this moment, the call is to save lives. And it is the right thing to do professionally, morally and spiritually. I had to swap my fear for faith. I need to remember the working power of the blood of Jesus; I need to trust God and remember that he is not slack in His promise.

The next stage was to speak to my family. I have had phone calls from my home country, Nigeria. My elder sister tried using her seniority to talk me out of my decision, but she was unsuccessful. She told me that she had never seen someone who would intentionally put herself /himself into such a dangerous situation. At last, she changed her tone from commanding to pleading with me to stop going to work. She expressed her distress about me as if I was not serious about my life—after everything that we see on the television, still pushing myself to nurse COVID-19 patients. She was terribly upset and asked me to make her a promise that I will stop working. I told her that I might consider it. (Anything to get her off my back!)

My husband and children had begged me to stop working, assuring that they will pay the bills. I told them that if it were about money, I would have been very happy staying at home. But in this situation, COVID-19 patients need nurses and doctors. I was seriously fighting two battles within my mind. One of the battles was, if anything happened to me it would be as if I asked for it and my family would never forgive me. I used to look at my children with everything going through my mind, even the worst-case scenario. My children looked at me with tears in their eyes and begged me to stay home because they were afraid lest anyone from our family would get infected through me if I catch the virus during my duty in the COVID-19 ward. However, I still refused to give up. I knew

I was working for a higher cause; the noblest of the causes in our times. I mustered up the courage and pretended to be brave before them and fended off their apprehensions. Nevertheless, behind the scenes, I was scared too. During their absence I walked up and down the house crying and praying at the same time, asking myself why I should do this. The question from my sister was beginning to play in my mind, *Do I truly love myself? What about my family and those that care for me?* These thoughts kept me exasperated day in and day out.

Though there was a lot of crying and tears, I had to answer the call of duty and carry on. I pleaded with my family to give me the permission and the support to do what I had resolved to do. I had to override family sentiments and concerns born of genuine love.

The spirit is willing, but the flesh is weak. When I recall that there are thousands of nurses out there, I have to find a way to think positively, knowing my presence was for a good cause. I must focus my mind on what I want; I have to call my higher-thinking self back to life and have the peace and joy to allow my low-thinking self to die for good. As I lay still on my bed, believing and trusting in God, no time to waver, no time to doubt, all will be well with me, is there not a cause? I seriously knew that my spirit was willing, but my flesh was weak. I cannot lean on the weak end of my life but count on the willing side of me for divine support.

CALLED FOR SUCH A TIME AS THIS

My confidence and faith in God over the situation were growing by the hour. I was determined to go back to work, and the shift had been assigned to me, after my days off.

I remember the ancient story of a queen called Esther in the Bible. She was married to a Pagan King of Babylon, Ahasuerus. Esther is often referred to as a Jewish queen married to a Pagan King. Ahasuerus' marriage to Esther was as a result of the rebelliousness of his queen, Vasti. Esther was chosen by the king to be his queen due to her beauty. Haman, who was the king's special adviser, had an issue with Esther's uncle and guardian Mordecai. Haman used his position to get permission from the king to annihilate all the Jews in the Kingdom in order to eliminate Mordecai. When Mordecai found out about the evil plot against his people, he sent a message to Esther. He told her about Haman's plot against the Jews and she had taken action by going to the king to prevent the evil plot. Esther replied to the message to her uncle that it is unlawful to go to the King without invite and moreover the King has not invited her for the last thirty days.

Esther's role is to save her people from the genocide plotted against them by going to plead on their behalf; she knew that this could cost her life. She was told by her uncle that if she did not use her position to save her people, God will raise someone else. And she, being a Jew, had no hiding place because she and her father's house will be burnt. He had told her "And who kneweth whether thou art come to the kingdom for such a time as this" Esther called for three days fasting and prayer among the Jews through Mordecai with her maid and herself included.
 She knew that her decision to go to the king could destroy her life, but she had said in her own words, "If I perish, I perish". Through her action and bravery, her people were saved. God

has called me for such a time as this (Esther: 2-10). I kept repeating this to myself. My name is Esther.

I am not sure how many times I have said this—it's about saving people's lives and I count myself privileged to be part of this. Queen Esther used her position to save her people; I as a nurse have also decided that I will use my position to care for the people that I am passionate about. As soon as the light bulb moment dropped in, I felt this unexplainable, massive bundle of joy within me, knowing that I am going to be used by God to save lives. It could have been me or my loved ones lying on a bed in any of the hospitals anywhere in the world. Someone must nurse and care for COVID-19 patients. I choose to be among the health care professionals in that role. I am called for such a time as this, I kept repeating it to myself, whenever I was discouraged, fearful and tired. I have to repeat it to myself constantly. The idea is to embed this into my subconscious mind; to bury my low-thinking self and embrace and welcome my higher-thinking self, who is positive and brave and fearless, knowing that I can do anything that I put my mind to because there is a greater power within me. I have always asked God to use me. God may not always use us in the poshest environment but will use us to relieve the suffering of mankind. That's why I have to ask my low-thinking self to rest in peace so that I can fulfil the call of my destiny. That is the story behind the name of this book, *CALLED FOR SUCH A TIME AS THIS.*

Although few wards are still COVID-19 patient free, the truth is that in the morning, at the beginning of the shift, the ward may start off as COVID-19 free, but before the end of the day, some of the patients may be tested positive or new patients transferred to a bay or two in the ward, or a side room may be used for patients that are COVID-19 positive. The best thing to do is to always prepare myself physically, psychologically and spiritually, knowing that I may be looking after COVID-19 patients. I now see myself as a soldier, and a good soldier does not run away from war, I keep telling myself. The role of a nurse is to save lives. That is exactly what I'm going to do. I have to use as many affirmations and prayers as possible in order to keep me psychologically stable.

CHAPTER 6

"MUM, I HOPE
YOU WILL FIND IT IN YOUR
HEART TO FORGIVE ME"

"MUM, I HOPE
YOU WILL FIND IT IN YOUR HEART TO FORGIVE ME"

It was a Thursday morning. Each nurse was allocated their different bay by the Junior sister of the ward. The ward manager came to the desk as we were about to depart to our different bays. "I have not enough patients for all of you to look after, as you all know that admission to the hospital is very minimal due to COVID-19," she said. "I will have to send some of you home and some of you will be transferred to other wards." In my mind, I said, *Let Your will be done, Lord*. She then took us aside and told us that we have a choice of going to Ward X or going home. We all knew that all the patients in Ward X were COVID-19 positive, and the other nurses said that they are happy to go home. Since the two of them and myself were from the nursing agency, she signed them for the two hours cancellation fee as per the agency contract agreement. I chose to go to the COVID-19 ward. The ward manager looked at me in disbelief, and she asked me if I understood that Ward X is now different; it is now a red zone. I replied that I was quite aware, and I'm happy to go there. So, l left for Ward X, and you should have seen the surprise mixed with concern on her face. I think I underestimated the workload in Ward X. All the patients were COVID-19 positive, but my PPE (personal protection equipment) was nothing to write home about. It was only plain surgical masks, and these were not really effective. The ward had a lot of respiratory patients on nebulizers and high-flow oxygen administered with different devices. Looking back now, I'm not sure how I was able to complete the shift.

After the nurse in charge had handed my patients over to me, I just said a short prayer in my mind, pleading the blood of Jesus. I had eight patients in total, and seven of them were very old patients who needed everything done for them (all care). I had a nurse assistant to help me. One of the patients was on palliative care, Mrs BD. She was on a syringe driver pump. A syringe driver or pump is used as part of palliative care to administer medicine subcutaneously to patients who are unable to manage or tolerate oral medication (Mukoreka and Sisay, 2015). It was useful because I did not need to continuously inject medication into Mrs BD to keep her pain-free since the pump is continuous for over twenty-four hours. Continuous subcutaneous infusion maintains a constant serum level of medicine (Barnes et al., 2009). Syringe driver pumps also reduce the need for the use of less popular routes of administration such as rectal or intravenous (Morgan and Evans, 2004).

I was told that Mrs BD may die at any time. I was also asked to transfer another patient whose COVID-19 result had come back negative, so I had to transfer her to the cardiac ward. Before transferring her, I stopped to ask the nurse in charge how long she has been in the ward, and what if she had caught the virus, considering that cardiac patients are at high risk. The result that came back negative was based on admission. However, the patient had been exposed to COVID-19, as she was nursed in the same bay with them COVID-19 positive. I was told that the bed had been allocated to a patient coming from another ward. Before I knew it, two health assistants had transferred the patient and all I had to do was hand over the patient's history and plans to the nurses in her new ward.

All the patients in Ward X were very unwell, coughing and sneezing and on back-to-back nebulizers. Some of them were in pain due to excessive dry coughing and I had to administer pain relief. We were so busy, one of the patients became very unwell and we were thinking of transferring him to a high-dependency unit while waiting for a bed to open up. It was difficult to feed some of the patients due to their coughing, which was almost nonstop. You could see in their eyes that they were exhausted and fed up, and I had to ask the doctors to change some of their medications to intravenous medications where possible.

I needed to take my break. I had to hand my patients over to another nurse. I had just a small window of opportunity to take my break; the restaurant is seven minutes away and I needed to be quick, as I had forfeited my first break. I had just that half an hour left for the day. I quickly used the ladies to freshen up, then went quickly in and out of the restaurant with my food. *Thank God there was no queue today*, I said to myself. As I was opening the door to get in, I came across our care assistant, who told me that Mrs BD had died. Her daughter alerted the team as she came to visit her and found out that she wasn't breathing. She died alone. At one point I had held her arm for a few minutes but soon left her to see to the other patients as the workload demanded. I never had time to go back to see her before my break. I felt as if I had let her down, as nobody should be dying alone. Mrs. BD's daughter (MN) was allowed by the doctors to visit her despite the restriction on hospital visits. I'm not sure why she was allowed to visit.

"Oh no!" I said on that news. I handed my food over to the care assistant as I dashed quickly to the room where Mrs BD was lying on the bed. Her daughter was sitting on the chair by her bedside. The patient laid there looking so lifeless but peaceful. I left the room to get the doctor to check her out. The doctor came quickly and certified her as dead. "I am sorry," the doctor said to MN. "I am sorry too," I said as I handed a box of tissues to her. With the help of the care assistant, we tidied Mrs BD up. I asked her daughter if she wanted some water or a hot drink, but she declined. I politely told her that I will be leaving her to spend some time with her mother and that I will be back soon with more information on what to do according to the bereavement booklet. I also told her that if she should need help before I come back, she was free to call me with the buzzer (I pointed at the buzzer). As I was about to leave, she said, "Please don't leave, as I will be leaving soon." I didn't understand why she wanted me to stay with her mother's corpse instead of her. I just couldn't see any sense in that, and I thought there was more to this. "If you're worried about being infected with COVID-19, I will get you all the PPE needed to keep you safe." She raised her head and said to me that she is not worried about the virus. Every member of her household had it. "I had taken mum into our house three weeks ago to spend time with us," she said.

The idea was for her to stay with them after the death of their father (the deceased's husband). MN felt her mother was becoming too lonely and the loneliness was taking a toll on her, hence they took her in to stay with them for some time before going back to her own home. She gently lifted her mother's left ankle; rubbing her lifeless toes gently, she pointed at her toe and told me that they went to the nail shop together where they both had their nails done and her mum had picked the bright pink colour that had always been her favourite colour for lipstick and nail polish. "Even old age had never changed it, nurse." She told me that they had so much fun and that was her mum's last outing before being taken to the hospital.

"Nurse, how do I live with myself?" At this time tears were streaming down her face like a river with no boundary. I bent toward her and said, "Sweetheart, it is not your fault. You were doing your best." "It's my fault," she said. "I got it and infected everyone else. It was like a mild flu at the beginning, but it was heavy on my husband as well. I caught it at work; there were three of us at work that had it, as we later found out. My girls are not too bad. I should have left mum alone in the comfort of her home. Mum, I'm sorry, you know this was not intentional."

I was so dumbfounded as I watched her lean on her mum, crying and pleading for forgiveness. "Mum, please find a place in your heart to forgive me," she sobbed.

I was speechless and felt helpless but full of empathy for her. I was imagining myself in the situation that she was in at that moment. Empathy, according to Pink, is the ability to imagine yourself in someone's position and to intuit what that person is feeling (Pink, 2006). It is the ability to stand in the other person's shoes, to see with their eyes, and to feel with their heart. I thought to myself that although it wasn't her fault, as a compassionate human this will haunt her for a while. I quickly said a prayer in my mind for her husband to pull through and for the world at large. *Merciful God, please take away this plague from the whole world.*

I left the room quietly to give her time to grieve, but her voice kept ringing in my ear. I went to see my other patients, to make sure that they were stable. The health care assistant that was assigned to me was amazing with the patients. She had a heart of gold; she was young, full of vitality and very caring. She seemed to enjoy her job very much.

I went back to the room to find out if there was any other member of the family that I could call to speak to MN on the phone, but she declined. She told me that her husband was in bad shape and she was not sure if he would make it out of the hospital. I encouraged her to stay with her mum for a while; she managed to stay for another one hour, for what I would call a most anguishing time. She just blamed and blamed herself so much that I'm not sure how she was going to live with herself and look after her sick family. *What a cruel world*, I said to myself.

I went straight back to work without having my lunch. As I was going around checking on the other patients' vital signs, the ward manager walked into my bay and asked if I was okay. "Yes, I am," I told her. But the care assistant interrupted by saying "No, she is not. How can Esther be OK if at three o'clock she had not had any break? Not even a cup of coffee or water."

"No," the manager said, "that is so unacceptable. Now go on your break while I keep my eye on your patients. Go and eat something." Thanking her greatly, without any hesitation I left the room. I thought that was kind of her indeed.

The break was not about food, but for me to reflect on what has just happened. This pandemic is like a horror movie. How does one console Mrs BD's daughter, MN, if her husband dies too? Everything from that scene was going through my mind.

As I sat there watching my food, the health care assistant opened the door and came in. "Are you not going to eat that food? Did you warm it up?" she inquired. I shook my head. "I will put it in the microwave for you," she said. "Thank you so much," I replied. I ate my food silently while reading the Bible from the app on my phone, following that with some silent prayer as there were other people in the room.

As I was about to leave the staff room, my phone rang. The call was from my agency consultant. He wanted to know about my day. I told him that he wouldn't want to know; that I ended up in another COVID-19 ward where I'd just lost a patient. I told him that although the death was expected, when a nurse loses a patient it just spoils one's day. You try to shake it off, but it's just not that easy to shake off the emotion. Together with what I had just heard from the deceased's daughter, the feeling and my thoughts of everything on that day were awful. In fact, the phone call came at the right time, because it allowed me to express my grief while speaking to my agency. I had bottled up everything that had happened until that time. I had tried as much as I could to be as professional as possible before Mrs BA's daughter. I have a very good relationship with my consultant, so at this time I permitted myself to relieve my soul of that emotion. Health care professionals have to accept the fact that they are human and are going to be acquainted with the suffering of others. It is always good to talk with someone else about how one feels; if you don't, it could be psychologically dangerous to hold everything in. With experience, you learn to control your emotions in front of the patient and their family and not allow the situation to prove debilitating to the work.

At the end of the conversation, my agency told me that he had a shift for me in a ward that is COVID-19 free. I knew that it wasn't going to happen that easy; it might start as free of

COVID-19 but, before long, half of the patients will be COVID-19 positive.

CHAPTER 7

GIVE MY DAD
A CHANCE

GIVE MY DAD A CHANCE

Back at work on the following day, the site manager came to the ward to take some nurses. She told the nurse in charge that she wanted two of her nurses to go to the new COVID-19 ward that had opened the day before. The site manager said that there was only one trained nurse in the New Ward, and I offered to go. There were so much PPE in the ward, more than I have ever seen anywhere, so at least getting PPE wasn't a problem. We were now only two nurses, but it wasn't long before the site manager, bless her, was able to get more nurses.

The patients were very unwell. Why did I volunteer to come here? I asked myself. After a few minutes of indecision, I made up my mind, took a few minutes to pray, and asked God for His divine protection over the team and myself. I prayed for the patients and their families. With the assurance that God was looking after me, I went to put on my PPE.

After the handover, the ward hostess told me that some of my patients needed to be fed. As I was about to go and start feeding them, I noticed that one of the patients, Mr PK, wasn't breathing. He was on high- flow oxygen but was not breathing. I quickly went to get the doctor. He came at once, assessed the patient and pronounced Mr PK dead. The death was expected, as I knew about his condition from the handover, but I didn't think it was going to be that quick. Mr PK died alone with his breakfast by his bedside. His family was contacted. They had the information on what to do after bereavement, but I wasn't sure how much information they were able to retain. His son with whom I had spoken to, kept asking the same question over and over. In the end, I told him that he was free to call the ward for further information or further clarification. Mr PK's children were told that the body would be taken to the mortuary and they could view him there.

The next gentleman, Mr TT, was on the highest amount of oxygen that can be administered in the ward, but it wasn't helping him. The oximeter had not been able to pick up the amount of oxygen in his blood. Why was he not transferred to ICU yesterday when he became acutely unwell? With the help of the care assistant, we repositioned him and supported him with pillows. He was a big man and too weak to assist. I managed to sit him up to give him some breakfast and his medication, but he appeared too drowsy for any oral intake and his intravenous fluid was in progress.

Another gentleman, Mr DJ was in the bed next to Mr TT. He was about 50 years old with a definite language barrier. I positioned his food for him and tried to make a sign for him to eat, but he refused. I tried feeding him, but he still refused. I spoke in English and also made signs that he needed to eat so that he can get better and go back to his family. He seemed to be staring into space. DJ appeared so sad, and later I found out that he was confused; he, had no contact address and no next of kin on his record and had been brought to the hospital by the police. *He looks well-kept, so he must have lived somewhere, I thought.* I wonder, *what on earth is happening in his life?* Suddenly, I noticed something on the floor—it was flooded with blood. I noticed that he had dislodged his cannula and removed his catheter while it was still inflated. I called for help, for his environment was flooded with blood mixed with urine. We quickly looked for the source of bleeding. He was bleeding from the catheter and the cannula.

The nurse assistant was dealing with the fluid on the floor, his vital signs were taken, and we had to put him back to bed. The doctors requested a blood test because he had bled so much. His Hb (Haemoglobin) was within safe range but his oxygen saturation was very low. He was therefore started on high-flow oxygen. His blood pressure was very low; the doctor had written him up for intravenous fluid, which commenced quickly to improve his blood pressure. As this gentleman was very sick, we needed to contact the family to update them on his condition, but the note stated that there was no fixed address or number. *What can I do?* I thought. He could not speak English, and I had no idea what language he spoke. The doctors were also aware of this and we were trying to find a way to trace his next of kin and find out the language he spoke. We were between a rock and a hard place—in my heart I was praying. It was bad enough for a patient to die in the absence of their family due to the lockdown. More distressing was not being successful in finding a next of kin. This condition in which the poor patient, the doctors and nurses found themselves is another level of stress.

Mr DJ was looking so weak, and you could see the fear in his eyes. His tired eyes seemed to be staring constantly at me. He seemed to be saying something, but the words weren't coming out. Even if they had, I might have not understood. I truly had a belief that he would be OK, but my problem was that I couldn't communicate this to him to let him know that all would be well and to reduce the level of anxiety. Although there were six people in the bay, no one was talking to each other. The only thing you heard was people coughing, and sometimes it appeared as if they were taking turns to cough. There was this particular gentleman who was coughing so much that I was becoming scared that he would pass out. You don't wish this for your worse enemy. I'll say his again and again COCVID-19 is evil.

I had to use body language to communicate to Mr DJ that he would be alright. He was now sweating; he had episodes of sweating profusely and shivering at other times. I went for a wipe, soaked it with water, and began to wipe his damp hair and face to cool him down. He then smiled, which increased my hope that he would be OK, though he was not talking at all. I used my hands to demonstrate to him that I need to call his family. The fear in his face seemed to be disappearing as he nodded his head. He pointed at his phone, which had been sitting on the table. Woah! This was magic. I got his phone and handed it to him. I helped him to hold it and he added his password, which he got wrong three times. But on the fourth try, the phone opened up. He pressed a number and handed it to me. The phone was ringing, I felt like jumping for joy but needed to be calm. I spoke to one of his friends and was able to get some information about him; we exchanged some channels of communication. I asked his friend to explain to him what was happening to him and to help him understand that he would be OK, just that it's going to be a matter of time.

The silence in the ward was broken by the sound of nebulizers during the afternoon drug round. Mr. DJ. was somehow stable, and I thought that was a job and a half. I then decided to move on to the other patients.

I was called by the ward coordinator to answer a phone call from Mr TT's children. He was another acutely sick man and his son wanted an update about his father. As I wasn't prepared to give him any distressing report over the phone, I handed the phone over to the doctor, who happened to be finishing the ward round. Due to the severity of the patients' health conditions in the ward, the ward was flooded with doctors. Mr TT's doctor was a lady and had a long conversation with his son and daughter over the phone. I could see that the doctor herself was distressed about the pressure on TT's children because of their father's health. I offered her a cup of tea, but she declined. It has been agreed previously that TT will not be resuscitated should his heart stop, but otherwise, he would get full treatment. Since that morning, he was not responding to the treatment. I had only met him that morning, and I was not sure why he was not taken to ICU the previous day. From the handover and medical note, there was evidence that he had a lot of medical input in the ward that he hadn't responded to. That morning, with his NEWS at 9, clinically, this patient ought to be in an Intensive Care Unit. NEWS is the latest version of the National Early Warning Score, first produced in 2012 and updated in December 2017. NEWS advocates a system to standardise the assessment and response to acute illness (NEWS, 2017). It might not have been possible due to the shortage of ICU beds during the pandemic. Unfortunately, such are some of the hard decisions that the doctors have to make. The allocation has to be for the most critically ill patient or those that will benefit more from the bed such younger patients.

The patient's family wanted their father to be taken to the intensive care unit, but the consultant had told them that he wouldn't benefit from it at this stage. As the family was not taking no for an answer, they had concluded that the patient should be given treatment with a CPAP. CPAP is a form of positive airway pressure, where a ventilator applies mild air pressure continuously. This keeps the airway constantly open for people who are able to breathe spontaneously on their own but nevertheless need help keeping their airway unobstructed (Werman et al 2004).

As this was being arranged between their doctors and the respiratory team, the family rang again to speak to me. When I took the phone, my intention was to tell them that the doctor had spoken to them and that I had nothing else to say. But it was not easy to escape from this phone call when I heard the distressed voices of the son and daughter as they pleaded with me to do anything to save their father's life. "Nurse please1" I told them to call me Esther. They pleaded with me to give their father food, and I had to explain to them why their father couldn't eat. "At least you can try him with soft food," they implored over the phone. I kept explaining but they were desperate. "Esther, please give him some water to drink." "He cannot take anything orally," I explained to them. I did not want to tell them that he was dying. I'm sure the consultant had tried telling them, but they were either not processing it or they did not want to accept it. "If you cannot give him anything orally, please feed him through the nose," they said. What they were saying was to feed him using a nasal gastric tube. I again had to tell them that it was not appropriate at that time—their father was not in a condition conducive for the process of putting in a nasogastric tube. And even if one could be inserted at that time, it would be of no benefit to him and would instead cause him even more distress.

Then they asked me to call a priest for the gentleman. I assured them that I'd do that. They shared their belief with me that prayer would really put their father's mind at peace, to which I agreed. Finally, they asked if they could ask me for a big and final favour, and I replied affirmatively. I was asked by Mr TT's son to go to his bedside; his pastor will be ringing his phone and I should pick it up when he rings and hold it to their father's ear as he prays. I agreed and did as they requested. As the pastor and his wife started praying, he tried to take the phone, but he was too weak! Did he understand the prayer? Did he recognise the voices? Was he looking forward to seeing or at least hearing from a familiar voice? I wondered what that meant to him.

I had to put the phone on loudspeaker as well as holding it close to his ear. The prayer was so touching, you could hear people crying and screaming "Daddy, Daddy, Daddy" in the back-ground. It was so heart-breaking. Mr TT became very agitated. That was not the state I wanted him to be in, but I didn't want to deprive him of this precious moment or deprive his family of the opportunity, as it may be his last chance for this encounter. It was such an emotional moment for us as a team. No one knew what else to do. At the end of the phone call, as I was walking to the nursing station, two porters were coming out with a body in their trolley from a side room. Mr TT was to be transferred to the same side room after it's was cleaned and where the CPAP will be started. I had promised his children that I would get a chaplain for their father as they had earlier requested. I went through the telephone operator to get the number and left the chaplain a message. Later the chaplain called back but only to tell me that he was self-isolating. He promised to seek another chaplain but warned me that all the chaplains might be self-isolating as well. In other words, I said to myself, there is no chaplain in the hospital at the moment. I was not going to let the family know about the chaplain not being available; I thought it would be very distressing for them.

As a nurse, it is always good to use one's discretion when dealing with things like this. When caring for a dying patient, you are caring for their family at the same time. One has to be careful how and what is communicated to them, at the same time be transparent. If they'd called me again about the chaplain, I would have told them that I had called the chaplain and was still waiting for one of them to come to us.

From his breathing, I knew that Mr TT hadn't long to live. The CPAP was not forthcoming, and, even if it had come, it was late. I'm sure that's why the doctors were dragging their feet. I was determined to defer my break as long as possible to make sure that Mr TT did not take his last breath alone. There was no chaplain in the hospital, and his family was not allowed to be there for him due to the restrictions imposed by the government, but there is a nurse by his bedside and that's why I am a nurse, to bridge the gap'. I stood there, wiping his face with a damp cloth and reminding him that he is loved by his family, but they were not allowed to come to see him due to the pandemic. I was unsure if he heard or understood what I was saying but I was saying these words with passion while adjusting his oxygen mask to make him more comfortable.

Suddenly, it happened. He was motionless; he had stopped breathing. I knew he was gone but the doctor had to certify him dead first. *The suffering is finally over*, I said to myself. I quickly went and informed the doctor to confirm the death, and she pronounced him dead. He looked so comfortable and so peaceful, as I told the Health Care Assistant who was helping me remove all the tubes that were attached to him. We both stretched out his body, covered him entirely with the white sheet, and tidied the environment. I allowed the doctor to call the family and let them know that he had expired. R.I.P. Mr TT.

I had to take my break after the doctor pronounced the patient dead. It was a mixed emotion for me—I was incredibly sad that he died but grateful that I was there holding his hand as he took his final breath.

It was already 1700 hours and I had not even had a cup of water or tea, apart from the cup of coffee which I had at home at about 0600 hours. I went to the staff restaurant. There were a few people in the restaurant, but everyone was socially isolating. It is funny how we socially isolate in the restaurant but cramp together in the wards. As I sat on the chair drinking coffee, I reflected on an eventful day. What could I have done better? Why was Mr TT not transferred to intensive care the day before? In my heart, I could still hear the voices of the children crying in the background while the pastor and his wife pray—poor family! In the end, I was grateful that I had the opportunity to look after COVID-19 patients and even more so to be there to see Mr TT through to the end.

I had called a few of my friends who are in the same career to see how they were faring during the lockdown and asked them about their work during this pandemic. They seemed to think that I was mad and didn't like myself. I knew that God is with me according to His promise that He will never leave and will never forsake me. Be strong and of good courage, fear not, nor be afraid of them: for the Lord thy God, he it is that doth go with thee; he will not fail thee, nor forsake thee (Deuteronomy 31:6).

I just thought to myself how much the word of God is alive. I am convinced that God had called me for such a time as this. I can only speak for myself. I am grateful that I have been able to be there for those patients and families, no matter what their outcomes. As I ate, I thought about how I now understood that my life is not my own. I whispered a prayer to God with a spoonful of rice in my mouth. I thanked God for the thousands of nurses who had put their lives on the line during this pandemic. I had been told that one of the nurses that we worked with a few days back had been admitted to an intensive care unit and was battling for her life. Another Health Care Assistant, who I cannot remember meeting, died not long after she felt the symptoms. There is a doctor for whom it took a CT scan of the chest to diagnose her of being COVID-19 positive, and she has been very sick in one of the COVID-19 wards. One can understand why some nurses had decided to stay at home, so it would be unfair to judge anyone about their decision.

Back in the ward after my break, the ward coordinator handed me a small slip of paper with a name and a telephone number underneath. I tried inquiring from her who the individual was, but she told me that she only answered the phone. The person, who she can only guess is a patient's relative, wanted to speak to me, hence she took the name and number for me to call back. As a matter of curiosity, I quickly went to the phone and called the mobile number. The voice was cracked as it was answered. The reception was very noisy, but I was able to hear a woman clearly as she spoke in between sobs. I can now guess that it was going to be one long phone call. I decided to pull the chair toward me, and I sat down. She introduced herself as YE, (Mr. TT's daughter) she started thanking me for being there for her father when none of them could. She said that she had promised him that she would do anything for him but, at his last and longest hour of need, desperation, pain and death, she and her family had failed him. Without interrupting her, I just listened. She told me that her father had single-handedly taken care of her and her sibling after their mother's death. She told me about his struggle, between home and work, to give them the best, especially when it came to their education. "He was our mother and father," she said.

I listened patiently and allowed her to pour out her heart through the phone. At the end of the call, she asked me to bin his belongings and tell the team of doctors and nurses, on behalf of her family, that they are grateful. *That conversation was a lot to deal with*, I said to myself. I was surprised how much my listening skills had developed in the few weeks of this pandemic. A lot of learning – from Neuro-Linguistic training and other personal development courses from the great trainer and teacher, Doctor Bishop Wayne Malcolm – has come alive. It reminded me of the neuro-linguistic presupposition that said that you never know how much you learn till you are ready to use it.

YE felt that they, as a family had failed their father, but even this is not their fault—it's because of the restriction in the hospitals as a result of the pandemic. So many families all over the world are going through this trauma, guilt, grief and sense of helplessness. Healthcare professionals have a lot to deal with. As I was pondering this, two porters walked past to collect another body. I shook my head—four deaths in one ward in one day. There are still more very sick patients for whom we have no idea if they were going to make it through the night.

On my way home I was too tired to think, but as sat on the train I got another phone call from my elder sister in Nigeria. "I have been watching and listening to the news from the United Kingdom and the death toll is unthinkable. These are human lives. We are aware that you are still working, and we are aware of the fact that we cannot stop you, but we are praying for you and your colleagues." "Thank you, sister," I replied. The call was short, for which I was grateful as I was not in the mood for a long phone conversation. When we finally

ended the phone call, wishing each other good night, I was relieved that she had finally gotten off my back and was doing
what she needed to do by praying for me, rather than trying to
stop me from what I needed to do. I'm not sure she can grasp
the bigger picture of the whole thing. Speaking honestly for
myself, as traumatising as some of the situations are for me,
I'm really happy to be able to play the role I do. That's why we
are on this earth—to look after one another in our individual
ways and to make the world a better place. While I was deep in
my thinking, I missed my stop by two stations. I would either
continue on a longer route or get back by two stops, but I had
a minute to make up my mind.

WHY WAS MR TT NOT TAKEN TO ICU FOR VENTILATION?

As I settled down on the train, the question came back to my
mind. I tried to dismiss it all the while but knew it was something I had to deal with in order to complete the shift in my
mind. I had asked the doctor why Mr TT was not transferred to
ICU the day before. Mr TT's son had also asked if their father
could be transferred to ICU and be ventilated. The doctor
had told them that the patient would not benefit from it. The
doctor had also told me that he would not benefit from ICU this
morning, but what about when he became acutely unwell the
day before? I hadn't time to read his full medical and admission
history but all I knew was that he was diabetic and obese as
well as COVID-19 positive.

Whether he had deteriorated on admission or while in hospital I couldn't tell. I could see his black and white trainers by his
bedside and his phone was still on charge. In light of the above,
Mr TT may have become acutely unwell while in the ward and
not on admission. So, the medical team should have escalat-
ed him to ICU. The oximeter could not pick up the amount of
oxygen in his blood, which means that he would have needed

more help than the type of oxygen device that he was on in the ward. I had promised myself that I was going to learn about the treatment of COVID-19 patients as much as possible. I knew that ventilation is a big issue and there is not enough equipment in the whole world; Britain is not exempted from the shortage. Apart from this, it doesn't make sense why a COVID-19 patient who is experiencing that level of breathlessness should not be ventilated—whether invasive or mechanical depending on the physician's choice, which in turn depends on the patient's condition. But why wouldn't he benefit from it?

It was my day off the following day, a Wednesday. I had decided to take Wednesdays off for the last two years, calling it my study day. My findings from my studies are evidence-based, as a lot of research has already gone into COVID-19 over such a short time which I think is brilliant.

Over 5-10% of patients with COVID-19 infection require intensive care surveillance and ventilatory support (Mohlenkamp and Thiele, 2020). The current recommendations suggest early intubation of COVID-19 patients for two reasons. One reason is for severe hypoxemia fulfilling the Berlin criteria of moderate to severe acute respiratory syndrome. The second is to protect staff from viral infection (Phua et al., 2020) and (Alhazzani et al., 2020). Some critical care physicians are questioning the widespread use of the breathing machine for COVID-19 patient, saying that a large number of patients could instead be treated with less intensive respiratory support; if the iconoclasts are right putting coronavirus patient on ventilators could be of little benefit to many and harmful to others (Begley, 2020).

Mr. TT was in severe hypoxemia, and from the Berlin Criteria, he would have been a good candidate for treatment with a ventilator in an intensive care unit. The previous day, the oxymetre was not able to pick up Mr TT's oxygen level. The gentleman would have suffered some organ failure. This was also documented by Begley, that the data from China suggested that early intubation of COVID-19 patients will prevent them from liver, heart and kidney failure. (Begley, 2020).

So, at the time Mr TT's family was asking for ICU, he might have suffered an organ or multiple organ failure. Could that be the reason why the doctor was saying that he will not benefit from ventilation? I knew from the time I took over Mr TT's care that it was too late for any intervention, but could he not have benefited from ventilation from the onset of his acute stage?

OBESITY AND COVID-19

Mr TT was obese and diabetic; however, his blood sugar had remained in the safe range, so that was not a problem. Evidence has shown that obesity-related conditions worsen the effect of COVID-19. There is evidence of this from researchers who identified the risk factor for COVID-19, among which obesity-related complications such as hypertension and diabetes were also documented. The studies carried out by Simonnet et al. showed a high frequency of obesity among patients admitted to intensive care for SAR-COV-2, and disease severity increased with BMI. Obesity is a risk factor for SAR-COVID-19 severity, requiring increased attention to preventive measures in susceptible individuals (Simonnet et al., 2020).

Another study was carried out by Chen et al., who investigated the characteristics of patients with coronavirus. The study shows that older people with comorbidities such as obesity or diabetes mellitus were more likely to have severe conditions (Chen et al., 2020).

In light of the above, Mr TT's history as a COVID-19 patient who is 75 old, diabetic and obese with respiratory failure, it was quite clear that he was at extremely high risk for the severity of the disease and that would qualify him for the Intensive Care Unit as soon as the warning signs were observed.

And at the end of the day, how does a doctor decide that a patient will not benefit from an ICU if the individual has not been given a chance? In my humble opinion, since Mr TT was an able man before the onset of COVID-19, doctors should have given him a chance. On the other hand, it could also be that there was no bed in any ICU or there was a younger patient who would have benefitted more from the bed than Mr TT. These are some of the hard decisions the physicians had to make.

The National Institute for Health Care and Excellence (NICE) had issued guidelines on how to decide whether to admit an adult with COVID-19 to a Critical Care Unit. The guideline was developed to maximise patient safety, make the best use of NHS resources, and protect staff from infection. The guideline states that irrespective of COVID-19 status, adults admitted to hospital should be assessed for frailty using the Clinical Frailty Scale (CFS) as part of a holistic assessment. NICE continued by advising clinicians to be aware of the limitation of using the CFS as the sole assessment of frailty—comorbidity and underlying health conditions should be considered. According to the recommendations, the risk, benefits and likely outcome of treatment should be discussed with the patient, carers and family using decision support tools (where available) so they can make well-informed decisions. The decision for admission to critical care should be made based on the medical benefit, considering the likelihood that the person will recover to the extent that the outcome will be accepted (Dean, 2020).

NICE states that CFS should not be used for certain groups of individuals such as younger people and those with stable long-term disabilities (cerebral palsy), learning disability or autism (Dean, 2020).

From NICE recommendations, it remains clear that Mr. TT may have qualified to be treated in the ICU. Now my question is: at what point was Mr. TT's family aware that their father was very unwell? Was there any discussion with his family regarding ICU at that point? Why did the discussion for ICU take place after the patient had deteriorated and not the day before, when it was observed that he was becoming critically unwell with a NEWS score of 9?

A patient with a NEWS of 7 and above needs a high emergency response. In Mr. TT's situation, he was on respiratory failure. He really and truly should have been transferred to ICU to give him a fair chance to live.

CHAPTER 8

NO STANDARD POLICY ON PPE

NO STANDARD POLICY ON PPE

One did not need to be told that the ward was a COVID-19 positive ward, but all we had were scrubs and thin surgical masks on our faces. The ward where I worked the day before had all sorts of PPEs. Everyone wore whatever they chose, not because it was appropriate to the setting but because it was available there. No one thought us which PPE to wear or the rationale behind them.

One of the girls had an MP3 mask; the infection control nurses came into the ward to tell her that it was inappropriate for the setting, and they had explained their rationale. I wasn't disputing their rationale but expressed my concern over the PPE to them. My concerns were based on my experience. Actually, there didn't appear to be a standard training in the whole NHS as to what PPE might be best in certain areas of COVID-19 wards. Every hospital was managing things depending on their PPE stock as against the needs of the staff, who have to be present 24/7 by a patient's bedside. I have observed during this pandemic that hospitals have argued and defended their preparations, arrangements and practices by all means. By training nurses in patches while they take their time and drag their feet in deciding who and who not to train, they are putting the nurses at risk. Any ward could be dedicated to COVID-19 patients at any time, depending on the inflow of patients to the emergency department. That's why everyone needed the training on the right PPE.

I had seven patients and one in a side room; the other six were in the six-bed bay. Those in the six-bed bay were all elderly. Three patients among them needed help to go to the toilet and the other three patients needed all care. One of them, a middle-aged woman, was very unwell. The door had to be closed all the time for infection control. The nurses were advised to spend the least time possible in the bays to protect themselves.

However, nurses can't spend less time than needed with a patient, as care will be compromised. Patients will always be patients; no matter what infection the patient has, they still deserve the best care. So, there is no question of spending less time with the patient. Nurses are responsible for their actions and their inaction.

NURSES CANNOT SOCIAL DISTANCE THEMSELVES FROM THEIR PATIENTS

If patients are unable to feed themselves, the nurses need to feed them. You have to take time to feed them; even when they refuse, the nurse still has to try to encourage them. Nurses have to explore if there is any other way of meeting their nutritional needs. The nurse has to make sure that patients are drinking, even if it is just some sips of water or other liquid, giving them a little at a time to avoid dehydration. The nurse has to monitor the patient's bowel movements and make sure that they are passing urine. Patients need to be kept clean, which involves performing or assisting with personal care. Meeting their hygiene needs and taking their vital signs—these are basic needs, but there could be a lot more depending on the patient's severity of illness. How can a nurse then spend less time with a patient? If any of the patients are confused, the nurse has to stay with them as closely as possible to keep them feeling safe. The time spent on a patient is determined by the level of their needs and not by choice. Every other member of the health care professional community can predict how long they are going to stay with a patient. In other words, nurses are very much at risk due to the length of time spent with patients and the close proximity required. To crown it all, a nurse can have as many as eight patients, so then the question is: how does a nurse spend less time with a patient? The answer is that it is impossible. As a result, one would think that adequate PPE would be available, but this doesn't happen in all the hospitals, from my experience as an agency nurse. That on its own puts the nursing staff at exceedingly high risk.

I had seven patients to look after on this shift, which I am grateful for because a nurse can often have more than seven. They all needed help. Three were all care and five could at least feed themselves. Among the six in the main bay, two were COVID-19 positive and four of them were not. The two COVID-19 positive had masks on but were not keeping them on because of their confused state of mind. As of that morning, two of the patients were discharged, one of them was waiting for transport, and the other was waiting for social service to confirm the care package before discharge. The patient that was waiting for transport suddenly got out from her chair and screamed, at the same time falling between her chair and the bed. Because I was closed by, I just caught her on time. As I was helping her back to her bed, I observed that she was stiff and appeared not to be breathing, I quickly pulled the emergency buzzer and the team responded in no time. She came back, after being reviewed by the doctors; all the recommendations made were carried out and the patient was settled. Later I heard the patient cry, and when I went to inquire about what the problem was, she told me that someone called to tell her that her mother was dead. The patient in question was 86 years old and we knew that she did not have a mother and she hadn't spoken to anyone on the phone. It wasn't difficult to figure out that she was confused. I took a urine sample and sent it to the laboratory. As her vital signs were high, and her temperature was very high as well, the other ladies' temperatures were also very high, so the doctor then asked me to do a COVID-19 swab test for the remaining four patients.

None of them would eat supper no matter how hard we tried. Two of the ladies were put on high-flow oxygen. One of the ladies was so confused that she was stripping herself; each time we went to her in the bay we would find her nude and inter-fering with other patients. The HCA and I had decided to take turns staying in the bay and monitoring her since she was at risk to herself and others. It was a bay with six potential COVID-19 patients with the door shut behind us.

Nurses sometimes subconsciously put their lives at risk for patients. This is exactly what we had done. If we hadn't, the patient might have fallen down, and that might result in serious injury, death or litigation. None of these is something a nurse wants to be part of. We need to prevent issues like this from happening. So really, to spell it out, during this pandemic the nurses are compromising their health to save the lives of others.

From experience, I knew that all the patients in the bay had caught the virus and one does not need the test results to know this. They were shaking and vomiting, and I had told the doctors. The nurse in charge had complained of fever and was asked to go home. The lady who was stripping was fighting with the nurses to get out of the ward. She is already out of the bay. The scene was so bad that the security officer had to be called in. He couldn't do much because our lady, bless her, was not causing trouble out of spitefulness but because of her mental state. She had packed her stuff and claimed to be going away. We tried stopping her, but it was difficult; she was into everything, hitting and spitting and attempting to bite anyone that tried to stop her. When the night staff came, you could hear prayers going out from the black nurses. God is our only saving grace now. The patient was into everything, but finally, nature took its course as she sat down on one of the chairs and began to nod. The night nurse had begun to clean the surfaces and the patient was escorted to her bed with a lovely mug of hot chocolate. Oooh, bless her and thanks to the kind nurse.

When I eventually took off my face mask, as I had been fasting all day. I could not recognise the woman looking at me from the mirror. It was a tiring day. I had red lipstick on that I had applied at about 0550 hours, and then there was my mask, which I'd occasionally remove for some sips of water. Looking at the mirror now without the mask, the lipstick appears as if I had been bleeding from my lips. My lips were cracked and dry and my eyes were tired and watery. Two other nurses and I left work two hours after the end of our shift as we waited to complete our documentation.

REFLECTING ABOUT THE SHIFT

The train was quiet, due to the lockdown, so I spent my entire journey reflecting on the shift. I thought about the two ladies who were discharged and were waiting for transport and care packages. As it is said: every disappointment is a blessing. Although the COVID-19 test done on them hadn't come back, I would bet that they will all come back positive. Why on earth, were they nursed among COVID-19 positive patients anyway? I wonder if it boils down to the bed situation. Are their families aware of this? How unethical was that for elderly patients coming to the hospital, to be nursed among confirmed COVID-19 patients? I was grateful that whatever it was with them presented itself before their discharge. They might have gone home and infected their loved ones if they were COVID-19 positive.

Also, the very sick lady, in my opinion, should have been tested as well before today. While she was not tested, it does not take rocket science to know that she had caught the virus. Yet treatment could not commence as long as she was not tested.

I feel that as a nurse looking after these patients that I should have asked to know why she wasn't tested, and why those patients were admitted in the mix of COVID-19 positive patients. This might make me seem like a troublemaker but as health care professionals we do challenge each other. No one is perfect, but in challenging, we improve our practice. It can sometimes be like a sort of checks and balances. Come to think of it, these days it can be a life and death matter. Anybody can become a patient! The golden rule is that you do unto one as you will like it done unto you.

CHAPTER 9

THE STRANGER IN THE TRAIN

THE STRANGER IN THE TRAIN

I caught the 2100 hours train to London Waterloo because I had missed the earlier one. I got off at London Waterloo East to change to the train coming from Charing Cross to Lewisham. Usually, I would have caught the train going straight to Hither Green, but for some reason, I had caught the train to Lewisham and subsequently needed to take a bus home.

It was about 2200 hours and I must have been the only one on the platform; the station was quiet, due to the lockdown. On entering the train, I still believed that I was the only passenger. As soon as I boarded the car and the door closed behind me, I heard a voice from the train. I was too frightened to process what the man was saying at first. "You are better off in the next coach because I'm going to smoke," he said. I was too scared to speak, but I wouldn't let him know how scared I was. "Why on earth would you smoke in the train?" I said as he lit the cigarette with a golden lighter. "I am going to smoke my head off tonight," he said. "Why would you do that?" I asked. He told me that he had just lost his father. "Ohhh, how?" I asked him. "To this f.........g coronavirus," he replied. I asked him which hospital his father was in and he told me the name of the hospital. I asked him how old his father was. He said that he was 65 years old. I consoled him and asked him to take care of himself. I said that I was so sorry about his loss. I went to the far end of the train to sit down, as I was too frightened to go to another coach. *Who am I to stop him from smoking?* I thought to myself. *If that is the only way to deal with his loss, why not? I cannot impose my standard on him.* Knight said that everyone makes the best choice available to them at the time they make it by believing that we can learn how to understand, coach high performance and forgive (Knight, 2008). That was the only way he knew how to deal with the present situation he found himself in.

I COULDN'T SMOKE AFTER I HEARD YOUR VOICE

I suddenly raised my head to see the gentleman standing and looking at me two rows of chairs away from where I was sitting. He was gentle enough to remember to socially distance himself from me, even in his present state of mind. My heart jumped as I saw him. With his eyes red, he began to speak in a deep, hoarse voice. He looked and sounded like someone who has been crying for a while. He introduced himself as AZ. "Who are you?" he asked. "I couldn't smoke after I heard your voice. Your voice was too strong, and I couldn't afford to light up. Who are you really?" "I am Esther," I said. He carried on with his reflection. "My father was an extraordinarily strong Christian.

Really, with my eyes enlightened, I knew my father had to die before going to heaven. But today I couldn't help myself, I didn't expect him to leave me so soon. We've been through so much together." He further said that his father hadn't given him time to give back to him.

He began to tell me about the death of his father. "He called one evening to tell me that he had the flu. He didn't think anything much about it as it was probably a common cold. The next day the flu was worse; his wife called 111, and he got some advice on the phone. In the evening he could not breathe, and his chest was very tight, so he was taken to the hospital." He told me that no one was allowed to visit his father and the next phone call told him his father was dead. He said that his thought was that it was an April fool joke from his friends until his stepmother called him and was crying on the phone.

"I have been drinking today and smoking; this is something I haven't done for years because of my religion," he remorsefully revealed. He told me that he couldn't help himself and the thought of seeing his father's cold body was driving him nuts. *What a life*, I thought. "Have you got anyone at home or friends that you can speak to?" I asked. He told me that he had, but as it was during this lockdown, none of them could come to him. I thought I had had enough at work today, but to face this in the train was challenging and well beyond me. He told me a lot of stuff that I am not willing to share in this book. In a nutshell, I will say that his life had been tough, especially during this pandemic.

"Please, sister, pray for me. You don't need to do it now, but I need your prayer," he said. He handed me some prayer leaflets he would have gotten from the priest or chaplain in the hospital after his father's death to help him cope. He sorrowfully said he wanted for me to have some of the leaflets. I stretched out my hands and collected the leaflets and thanked him as he disembarked the train at London Bridge station. Suddenly, I heard someone saying to the train operator, "Wait, I have to give something to my sister." He jumped back in the train and handed me another set of prayer booklet with four silver ornaments (I couldn't figure out what they were or what they were used for). I was in a state of fear, panic or shock as he was handing over the stuff to me. I had just about time to thank him when he jumped out of the train and the door shut behind him. I felt like leaving everything that he handed over to me in the train, but that thought was aborted as I did not want to be ungrateful. He was doing his best.

As I opened one of the booklets, something fell out of it. It was a plastic bank card. Initially, I thought it was a fake card but on a closer look, I noticed that it was the real thing. It was a platinum Visa card. He had told me his name, so I knew that it was his; this was in addition to what I was going through, already. I became very emotional. I felt so sorry for him. What if his travel that night depends on that card? *It was a Friday night and how could he manage over the weekend?* I thought. His father's death has taken a toll on him. I knew he had asked me to pray for him, but the immediate prayer I did for him at that moment was that we'd somehow meet so that I can hand the card over to him. I prayed this while disembarking from the train in Lewisham train station. I stood by the side of the road waiting for my daughter to pick me up, hoping that he would come round.

As I stood there, I thought about how easy it is to pass judgement on others without understanding their world—where they are coming from and what makes them behave the way they do. All we see is the surface, the visible, the obvious, and we pass judgement. We measure ourselves against others. If only we could take out time to listen, love and care, we would be less judgemental; we would learn to love our neighbours as ourselves, pray for them and allow God to take control.

My daughter pulled up to pick me up. "You looked so spaced out, Mum. What happened?" I told her that I was only tired, but grateful that it is a Friday night as I'm at home for the weekend. The following day I disclosed to my daughter everything that had happened. The visa card was destroyed, and the booklets and the silver stuff were put in a little plastic bag under a stool in my living room. Up till the time of this writing, they are still there; I have neither read nor opened the booklets but haven't had the guts to bin them.

CHAPTER 10

NOBODY WEARS PPE IN MY WARD

NOBODY WEARS PPE IN MY WARD

O n getting to the ward that I was assigned to, I found it was shut. I rang the bell but there was no reply. On closer observation, I noticed that the ward was closed and there was a sign on the door saying where the ward had moved to. When I got to the new ward, the handover was about to start. I went to the changing room expecting to find some PPE, but there was none. I asked one of the night nurses where I might find some PPE, and she told me that the ward is COVID-19 free; as such, the staff in the ward are no longer allowed to put on PPE. The nurse directed me to the ward where I was likely to get some PPE. I quickly went to the ward and the manager there was kind enough to allow me some PPE from her ward. We both agreed that at that time, with the number of newly diagnosed cases and the number of deaths among the health care professionals, it's only fair for the trust to continue to provide us with PPE. In addition to that,we nurses need to be there for one another. I went back to the ward with just a standard PPE.

On getting to the ward I heard the ward manager giving a long talk about why no one in her ward is allowed to wear PPE. She wasn't even allowing anyone to wear a face mask. *Really?* I wondered. A few days prior to that I had received an email from the Nursing and midwifery council intimating that Nurses have the right to walk out of the ward if they are not happy with the PPE provided. The email continued by saying that nurses are in their role to save lives, not to die. The manager had claimed that she knew so much about the disease and its conspiracy theories that no one can tell her anything about COVID-19. She had asked that if anybody wants to know about the virus, they should come to her. The night nurse, who was also in charge of the night shift nurses, had told her that if she got infected, she would be going to Human Resources to make a complaint about the manager.

I quickly interrupted by saying that even at that point it might be too late—after being infected and then going to Human Resources. I told the manager that I needed to remind her that even the World Health Organisation does not understand the disease, so how could she be so confident in saying she knew so much about it. I reminded her that if anything happened to anyone in the ward, she might not be there to repeat whatever she had just said. At that point, I opened my phone and showed her the email from the Royal College of Nursing. I told her that I was leaving the ward as I didn't feel safe enough to work in the environment. Experience has shown me that before 1200 hours, the doctors would be coming to tell nurses how many patients who had COVID-19 swabs were positive. When I turned around, I saw the doctor who was on the nightshift. She had on full PPE, so why are the nurses so ill-treated? I wondered if we are sacrificial lambs or what? Why are the nurses enemies to themselves? If doctors can put on masks in the ward, why can't nurses put on masks?

"I did not say you should not use PPE," the ward manager said, contradicting herself in the presence of her staff. She then pleaded with me to stay. At that point she said had no issue with whether or not I wore my PPE. The other staff, at least this time, had the nerve to put on their face masks.

With my PPE on, I went to see my patients to make sure that the handover that I got from the night nurses was the same as their current status in terms of their wellbeing. As I was on round to see the patients, one of them told me that she had an awfully bad night. She wanted to give me some more information, but she was too breathless to continue. I had to tell her to stop and that I would come back to her. The patient next to her told me how she was shivering and appeared to have been in so much pain through the night. Although I listened to her, there was nothing new that wasn't handed over. In the end, I made her understand how grateful I was about the information.

I was asked by one of the patients to put on some music. "We have no music here," I replied. Another patient told me that they had music the previous day. We need music, they continued.

One of the nurse assistants told me that it was the hospital radio. I reassured them I would sort that out in a bit, but they weren't taking that for an answer. I went to one of the women who told me that she had a really bad night to find out from her why she had a bad night. I then took some vital signs. While I was doing this a God-sent lady, Ms Green, walked towards me and stood in front of me. We both introduced ourselves, she told me that she has been deployed from another department of the hospital that is closed and she has come to help me out. I was really grateful for that. While we were talking about the hospital radio, it came on air and a song from the 1970s was being played.

It was a song that was well known by the patients in the bay. Ms Green seemed to be familiar with all the songs that came on that morning. She was so good that I told her she was in the wrong profession. "You need to see Simon Cowell." We both laughed along with the patients, but I meant it. As Ms Green sang along, she was also making some lovely moves and the patients looked so happy; they complied with their care and feeding that morning. They were all happy to get out of bed except the unwell Mrs CC. Some of the patients followed the nurse's moves as much as they could. The whole atmosphere was changed through her few hours with us until she left for her break. *That was seriously impressive,* I said to myself. The effect of music on patient care is not something we nurses often think about. The songs, the music and the dance changed the patient's mood.

Music perception was demonstrated in a narrative review that explored the effect of sound and music in hospital settings. Music intervention in health care can have a positive change in patient-reported outcomes, such as eliciting positive emotion and decreasing the level of a stressful condition (Iyendo, 2016). Listening to soothing music has been shown to reduce stress, blood pressure and post-operative trauma when compared to silence. In the research, it was found that sound conveys much meaningful information that is positive for both patients and nurses than listen to the sounds of soft wind, bird twitter, and ocean waves (Iyendo 2016).

While the patients were having fun with the music and the beautiful songs, the doctor came to review my unwell patient. The result of her COVID-19 swab had come back from the lab. I saw the doctor speaking to the ward manager. Guess what? Mrs CC had been tested positive for COVID-19, and she had been in an open bay with five other patients. The doctor had informed her family that she was very unwell, and she might not pull through, from the look of things. The doctor had been communicating with the daughter since her admission, but today it was a more serious conversation. We were asked to transfer her to the side room for her dignity. We had made her comfortable and monitored her for any sign of pain.

I wasn't going to allow her to die alone. Although none of her family members were around, as expected during the lockdown, she had the nursing team by her side. Her daughter had been on the hospital iPad and was able to see her. She knew that something was definitely wrong as the conversation was only one-sided. She had tried kissing her mother through Facetime; she had wept her eyes sore but there was no real human touch. I had tried to whisper in CC's ear that her daughter was on the phone talking to her, but she was getting deeper and deeper in her sleep. We all knew that her time was coming closer.

The other patients had sensed what was happening and were quiet. None of us spoke about the patient but we could read between the lines and they were afraid. It was a mixed bay; I'm not sure why. One of the three men, Mr JM, had been discharged and would be going home that afternoon. I asked the doctor if I should swab him for COVID-19, but he declined. I knew that there are protocols for swabbing COVID-19 patients, even if the patient is well and hasn't shown any symptoms. That's where the problem lies, as the incubation period takes a while. Then again, if any of them had contacted it, they may never show any symptom although they can pass it on to someone—someone who may become very unwell with it and may even die, as it stands. They could infect their loved ones at home. There is no answer to this, as patients cannot be kept in the hospital when they are fit to go home. It is like network marketing in the coronavirus world. In my opinion, it would have been wise to test these patients before discharge, then ask them to isolate themselves as much as possible at home. At the end of the day, it is about keeping people, families, loved ones safe and keeping our communities, countries and world free from the pandemic.

THE GAME-CHANGER

The next thing I saw was the manager, wearing a face mask and goggles. I looked at her without saying a word. As the saying goes, "Actions speak louder than words". She got up quickly and went to the clinical store and got some PPE, masks and goggle pieces. She then started distributing them to staff. What had changed? Two patients in the ward had tested positive for COVID-19. Was I surprised? No, no, no, and I guess none of the staff was surprised either. But people were too scared to speak out and they put their own health at risk. Nurses are encouraged to be assertive. I remember when I started my first job as a nurse, among the courses that we attended during our induction was an assertiveness course. Nurses should be assertive enough to preserve the rights of the nurses as well as the clients who are seeking nursing care. Assertiveness by a nurse shows a behaviour that is based on certain principles such as equality, respect and responsibility (Mushtaq, 2018).

When the night staff came back to work that night, they were grateful that I was assertive that morning. It was mind-blowing when the night nurses were talking about how they had to start their morning rounds with patients earlier than the normal time to be able to use PPE before the manager came in at 0630 hours. According to the nurses, as soon as she sees them wearing PPE they will get into trouble. Nurses are there to save lives and not to put their lives at unnecessary risk. This is because if a nurse is infected and dies as a result of COVID-19, it is the deceased's family that suffers as much as the families of those hospital patients who have gone down during this COVID-19 crisis. No matter how much the government pays those families, there is something money cannot buy—money cannot take away the emptiness, the emotion, the vacuum, the disruption created by death. Time may be a healer, but the pain will never completely go away.

"THE MASK HAS BEEN EXPIRED FOR FOUR YEARS"

The nurses were very excited about my intervention about the PPE. One of them went to get another nurse and said to her, "Nurse XX, this is the nurse that I was telling you about with regards to PPE this morning." They had gathered in the staff room to thank me for the intervention. One of the nurses said that what struck her most was the fact that I was able to stand my ground even as an agency nurse. I had encouraged them to be assertive and always put their point across in the politest way possible. I had to show them the email sent to me by the Royal College of Nursing. I told them that it was an abuse of power and against their own rights to work in an unsafe environment at this time of pandemic.

One of the nurses left the room and came back with one of the masks. It was an MP3 mask. She told me that even that mask, the one the manager was depriving them of using, had expired anyway. "Really?" I asked her how she knew about that. She told me that there was an email about it. She opened her NHS email and showed it to me. She then took the mask, showed me where a little sticker was stuck on to conceal the expiry date. She then took off the sticker, and it showed that the mask was expired by four years. Although the date was fading away, it was still visible enough for the naked eye to read. My mouth was agape! I thought that I had seen and heard it all, but this was another level. She told me that the management had told them that they were still protected.

What else was happening with the asset management and how come the masks were still in stock all these years? Were they just delivered to the hospitals? It made me begin to question what else we didn't know. What else had been concealed from us, how did they decide to put stickers on face masks, and what else has been kept from us? On the other hand, I'm not going to blame the trust so much, as they had the decency to email their staff about it. In the email, they were told that they were protected. Really, in such a case, why did the manufacturer have a date on the mask? Is it just to tick the box or there is something in the mask that will not be effective in terms of protecting the users after a certain date? Now someone is telling us that it's okay, you are still protected. Are those who are sending these emails working with COVID-19 patients in the bays while they are coughing and sneezing? Are they there while the nurses are giving nebulizers to the patients? I wonder how the management knew that the users were still protected. On the other hand, I still applaud them for their transparency. At least the staff knows they can trust them. When an organization is more transparent with their employees, they tend to be more successful. This type of environment leaves the employees feeling valued. Transparency fosters a type of comfort that allows employees to communicate effectively and thus progress (Miller-Merrell, 2019).

As I left the ward that night, I went to do a bit of research on how effective expired masks are. I found out that a GP practice nurse in England had raised an alarm after receiving PPE that had a sticker covering the old expired date and was rela-belled with a new date. That image was posted on social media showing batches of PPE that expired in 2016 relabelled as going out of date in 2021.

There were reasons for the action, as we all know that the world is facing a shortage of PPE. NHS supply and Public Health England, as well as the manufacturer, therefore decided to test the PPE for their safety, and they relabelled all the products that passed the tests and had their expiration date changed. Dr Matt Mayer, Chief executive of the local medical commit-tee covering Berkshire stated that "We are hearing from prac-tices all over our area that the PPE being sent to them is inad-equate. To now find out that PPE is not just out of date, but that the expired date has apparently been deliberately concealed is staggering." (Gilroy, 2020). I find this especially appalling because those responsible for the relabelling of that PPE are not on the frontline. Another issue is that it is deceptive. They would have been better off leaving the expiry date that came with the product, then informing health care professionals that although the PPE is expired the masks have been tested and they are fit for use. In my view, that would have been the most honourable and decent thing to do, allowing the user to make an informed choice on whether to work with expired masks or not. And if they do choose to use these, they can take extra precautions, knowing that they may not be hundred percent protected.

Otherwise, for me, it is misleading the users and deliberate-ly putting the frontline workers at risk. What if the practice nurse or someone did not find out and raised the alarm? To be quite honest, that has knocked my confidence in the system off the wall. The NHS, which has advocated for transparency, can conceal and change the expiration date of an important piece of equipment that has everything to do with the life of the frontline workers in this pandemic. There must be a lot of other things they have concealed, in my opinion. The public and the healthcare professionals who are on the frontline may never know if the death of doctors, nurses and other frontliners were linked to expired PPE. At the end of the day, the decision-makers might never have been anywhere close to any of the hospitals during this pandemic. The consequences of expired masks may never directly affect them in any way. I look at this as inconsiderate and morally wrong. My question is: if they or their loved ones were among the frontliners, would they be confident to work or allow others them to work with COVID-19 patients while wearing expired masks?

THE STRESS OF WASHING MY HAIR EVERY NIGHT

On my way home, as I reflected on the issue of expired PPE, I became really concerned about my safety and that of our families. Nurses, who are with patients for twelve and a half hour shifts, being forced to use expired masks? A nurse had told me that she had to live in the spare room in her house and refused to have her children cuddle her. Even the thought of washing my hair every night was adding to my stress. The hospital had provided a bathroom for every ward so that nurses can have a shower before going home. Come to think of it, in a ward with about ten or more staff in a shift, including the doctors, how can everyone possibly use the bathroom? Even if they could, everyone using the same bathroom is not safe.

The idea is for us to wash our hair before going home, for infection control. As a black woman, I feel sure many like me can agree that this not exactly the best policy, as most people of my shade either wear wigs or plaits. At this time around I had plaits that were awfully long. It happens that I have to wash my hair every night. It takes a long time to dry, and sometimes I have to sleep with wet hair. My pillows were always wet, and although my husband did not complain, I knew that he wasn't happy about the whole thing either. One morning I woke up at 0430 because I was so worried about my hair that I had hardly slept. I took up my scissors and lowered my head in the bin in my bedroom. I first of all cut off all the plaits, then went ahead and shaved off all the hair. Then I showered and went to work. I have never regretted that action, looking back on it today. What matters to me is my health and that of my family—it was no longer about my looks.

CHAPTER 11

"WE WERE BROUGHT IN TOGETHER BUT SHE COULDN'T MAKE IT"

"WE WERE BROUGHT IN
TOGETHER BUT SHE
COULDN'T MAKE IT"

On entering the ward, one doesn't need to be told that every patient in the ward was COVID-19 positive. In fact, these days I prefer working in a COVID-19 ward rather than COVID-19 free ward, as I know in advance that most of the patients will be tested positive anyway. This day the workload was not too heavy and one of my patients was self-caring. Mr Q, as I will call him, was well enough to be discharged home. His transport was booked for 1000 hours. I wished it could be delayed until after lunch so that he would have had his lunch before going home and would not have to worry about his lunch when he gets home. I worry about this a lot – sometimes I have to delay the patient's discharge time until after lunch – because some of the patients live on their own. One can argue that this does not help in terms of the bed situations but relieving somebody of the anxiety or worry about what to eat at home as soon as the ambulance drops them off is really important. It just gives them enough time to settle back in their homes before calling for help or deciding to go out for shopping. Again, it depends so much on their ability, as some of the patients may *never* be able to go out for shopping and will depend on social service or family.

Mr Q's medications had arrived from the pharmacy, but the doctor had added more medications and we had to wait for that to arrive before discharge. Usually, we could allow him to go home and get someone to pick up the medication, but due to the lockdown and strict visiting regulations at the hospital, it was best to wait for the medications to arrive so that he could go home with everything at once.

"Could you remove my cannula so that I can get ready to go home?" he asked as he was making his way to the restroom for a shower. "Please sir, I will remove it just as soon as you are about to go home," I said. "It is important to leave it in there just in case the doctor prescribed you more intravenous medication or anything that might warrant intravenous access later." He wasn't happy with that answer. It is always a good practice to remove the cannula just before a patient leaves the ward because it is not unusual for a patient to become unwell after they have been discharged, but he is still in the ward waiting for their medication to take home or transport.

"Lunch is here, Mr. Q, I'd like you to eat before the transport arrives, as it is now booked for 1315," I told him. "Thanks,

Esther," he said. Then I went to collect his medications and cross-check them with the nurse in charge. I removed the cannula and finally advised him on how to take the medications and what each of them was used for. Just as I was speaking to him, an ambulance crew arrived with a wheelchair to pick him up. Mr Q sat on the wheelchair with the bag containing his belongings on his lap. "Who is at home sir, your wife?" I asked. "No, there is no one at home. Both of us were brought in but she couldn't make it," he told me. "What are you talking about?" I exclaimed with distress. He explained, "I mean we caught the virus; we were brought in together to the hospital, and then she died." "You mean just on this admission?" I asked because I was not sure if I understood what he was talking about; it didn't make sense to me. "Yes, she died two weeks ago," he told me. I held my head with my two hands, I was so shocked, but I managed to ask him how, what and where. He told me, "In this hospital and of COVID-19." I tried to put myself together or pretend to be strong. "Who is at home now?" I asked him again. I meant: when he got to his house who would be there? He spoke in a hollow voice that no one would be there. I asked him if he had no family. He told me that he had children, but they lived far away, and, of course, because of the lockdown, they couldn't come to him. On my constant interrogation, he remarked "Please don't start me off, Esther." He would have noticed that I too was holding back my tears. "I'm sorry sir," I said.

Then, lost in the memory of his late wife, he started revealing. "She was such a lovely girl. She had cancer, she had beaten it, and had been doing so well. I had planned the holiday of a lifetime before the lockdown for nearly all the world." I stood by him in his wheelchair, speechless. The porter that came to pick him up stood there motionless like a statue. Usually, the porters are always in a hurry and can hardly wait in the ward for five minutes. We both looked at some pictures on his phone. They both looked so amazing; they were absolutely made for each other. It wasn't difficult to see that they had seen a lot and lived life to the fullest. As he switched off his phone, he looked straight into my eye and said, "Esther, where do I start from? I am going to an empty house. A few weeks ago, I had my beautiful wife with me in the house, but today I will begin to learn to live alone. It will be a long, lonely and painful day to come. My beautiful KH has gone, but her spirit and sweet memory will live with me forever." I was frozen, but tried to be as professional as possible, or at least pretend to be.

"I suppose there is no food at home?" I expressed my sympathy to him. "I suppose there is, it's okay," he replied. I requested Mr GW (the porter) not to wheel him away and I would be right back. I ran to the kitchen, grabbed a pint of semi-skimmed milk, a chicken sandwich, found a pot of yogurt and 200 ml of orange juice. As I was leaving the kitchen, the ward hostess saw me and protested. "You are not allowed to take the food; it's for the patients!" she shouted. "I will report you to my supervisor and the ward manager." I ignored her and continued on my mission. *I have unfinished business,* I said to myself. I needed to get to the patient before the porter wheeled him away. "I have this for you, Mr Q." I handed over the food bag to him on approaching him. "That's very kind of you, Esther," he said as he was wheeled off the ward.

I was dumbfounded on my way home on the train. How can this be, and where will he start from? I understood his wife's death, but to go home in an empty house from the hospital was another thing—no family to grieve with him. In the train, I prayed for Mr Q and his family. As I prayed, it dawned on me that there are so many people like Mr Q in the community, who have lost their loved ones and have no support. It reminded me of the church called ICC—they have a ministry called TOUCH, and it is one of the many charities that supports people like Mr Q in the community. I know that people of faith are praying. I realize that this is a war and we are in it together, everyone playing their part.

CHAPTER 12

TENDER LOVING CARE AND DIGNITY

TENDER LOVING CARE AND DIGNITY

The next day, after the handover, I went straight to the patients allocated to me to make sure that their conditions reflected the handover that I got from the night staff, and I wanted to introduce myself to them as well. The round gives the nurse and the patient time to meet each other, and here we find out if they have had a good night's rest. The nurse might ask questions like: did you sleep well last night? This opens a dialogue between the nurses and their patients. Some might say things like: it was difficult to sleep outside my home; I couldn't sleep because of the noise from the nurses; that patient opposite/next to me was snoring too much; she was chatting on the phone all night; the pain, ooooh, the pain, nurse; I couldn't sleep but I didn't want to disturb the nurses because they were busy; they have so much to do so I didn't want to disturb them; there are people worse than me; at last, nurse, I had to ask for pain relief; I only got to sleep at 0400 hours; and, that was the best sleep that I have had for days, etc.

"Good morning Mr ZE," I said to the 86-year-old man lying on the bed with half of his face covered with a dressing and an oxygen mask. He'd had skin cancer on his face that was removed weeks before coming to the hospital, and the dressing was still on the left side of his face.

It was not certain where or how he caught COVID-19. "How are you sir, did you have a comfortable night's rest?" I asked. He said, "Not really." "Oh, why not?" I asked. "I really want to get back to doing things for myself like I used to," he said. "Things like what, sir," I asked. He explained that he liked going to the toilet by himself, washing himself, and preparing his own little meal with his wife. "Who said that you cannot do those things anymore?" I asked. "The B-------- doctors," he replied. I solaced him by explaining, "No sir actually, the doctors are truly kind people. They are looking out for your own best interest. You don't want to have a nasty accident by falling down on your way to the toilet. I am sure sir, you know when people are unwell, they become weaker, but as they get better, they begin to rebuild their strength." "I suppose you are right, nurse," he sighed. "I need to use the toilet, nurse, are you in the position to help or should I use the buzzer?" he asked. I gently sat him down on the bed, but he looked so frail and breathless, I had to take him on a wheelchair with a portable oxygen cylinder.

On our way back from the toilet, the doctors were waiting to see him. The team of doctors exchanged greetings with Mr ZE. In the middle of the examination, he was asked about his social circumstance. He told them that he lived with his daughter, his wife was... He couldn't finish the sentence. "What is it about your wife, sir?" one of the doctors asked. Mr ZE started to weep and told them that she was dead; she died a year ago. Everyone around expressed their sorrow for his loss. After the examination, the doctors left. I pondered about it while dispensing the medications: she was dead a year ago, but he wanted to go back to her so that they could do things the way it used to be. I'm not sure why he was still crying. "Sir, I have your medications." I handed the pot of medicine over to him and turned back to give medication to the next patient.

Two physiotherapists came to see Mr ZE; he told the physiotherapist that his problem was that he was not allowed to do anything on his own. The physiotherapist reassured him that as soon as he was strong enough, he would be able to walk and do things by himself. The therapist asked him if he lived with his wife, and again he started wiping tears from his eyes. I was curious—what was it about his wife that made him shed tears? Old people and marriage—what it is that bound them so much together that it breaks them when one is no longer there! Is it love or companionship? I wondered. As the therapists were about to leave, I called to them. I told them that the gentleman looked like someone who might benefit from a psychologist, that he sheds tears any time he hears someone talking about his wife. My other concern is that his wife had died a year ago, but he wants to go back to her so that they can do things the way it used to be.

He agreed with me on the idea of a psychologist, but he exclaimed that the problem was that it might be difficult to get one due to the lockdown. Mr ZE's daughter previously rang me to explain to me about his medication, then she again called for an update. I told her to hold on or ring again after 10 minutes so that I could check his record. Actually, I had to ask for Mr ZE's consent before giving out his information. Ideally, we are not supposed to give out this information over the phone, but with the present situation, we haven't got a choice. Mr ZE permitted me to speak to his daughter. I thought it was a good opportunity to find out the reason for his crying every time we tried to talk about his wife. After the update, I told his daughter that her dad cried every time we talked or asked questions about his wife, who I guessed would be her mother.

"Yes, she was the most amazing woman. I had taken dad in after her death as he was inconsolable." She told me that before the onset of all this, he had refused for anyone to cook or do anything for him. "He was so close to Mum. They met when he was 18 and she was 16 and got married two years later. They did not have biological children (I was adopted), but they were such a lovely and happy couple," she said. *I am not sure whether it is love or companionship, I said to myself.* "Thank you," I said. "I will communicate this to the team," I told her. I went back to Mr ZE. "Sir, we need to talk," I said. He seemed to be all ears. "Sir, I do not want to upset you any further than you already are, but what is it that makes you cry whenever in your conversation we mention your wife?" "I want to go home, but I know she is dead. Her spirit is there. I do not want to go to my daughter's because I have the coronavirus," he said. "She has three young children and a husband who's diabetic. I do not want to infect them. With all this in mind, it will be best if it were all over. I don't want to be an old fool with all my burden on people." He began to cough as he spoke. He was coughing for a long time, with tears running down his eyes. I gave him a glass of water. He was shaking so I held the cup for him while he gradually sipped. He told me that the shaking started after he caught the coronavirus

Mr ZE took some tissue from the table and gently wiped his mouth. "Sorry, Esther," he said. "You don't need to apologize," I assured him. "It is very painful when I cough," he said, "When I cough, my body aches so much as if my ribs are going to crack. I want to go to my own home. I know that's where my wife's spirit is and that's where she wants me to be. She is there waiting for me to come home," he sighed. I wondered if he was confused, but that was unlikely. I had to tell the doctor about his concern for his family. The only thing is that because of the lockdown there was not a lot we could do. "I do not want to infect my family. They are all I have," he remarked mournfully. It was time to take his vital signs. I took his temperature, which was very high, and the vitals were higher than ever. He was a sick man. This time I called for help to assist him to bed because he was weaker than when I met him in the morning. I called the doctors to come and review him. His bloodwork and all the clinical tests were taken. He was only for ward ceiling of care, the doctor said. That means that he wasn't for the High Dependency and not the Intensive Care Unit. Should his heart stop, we could not attempt to restart it again. He was very sick, and we had to take frequent observations. We called his daughter to tell her how unwell he was. I had to put her through the ward iPad so she could speak to him, but none of what he was saying made any sense. Mr ZE's daughter was on the iPad for a long time. "I hope he is not going to die," she said. She told me that they had sorted out his house for him and were in touch with the social service about the new arrangement and they didn't live far from each other. She told me that she was going to take care of him when he gets home. Poor daughter, she had no idea that things had changed. I got the doctor to speak to her again, to tell her how it was, and that he might never come home again. I told her that I would keep her posted and reassured her. Hmmm, I wonder what it is with elderly people. Is it just love or companionship? I keep repeating this without knowing why.

The doctor had told me that Mr ZE was likely to die. His oxygen was dropping, so he was placed on high-flow oxygen and transferred to a side room, where he was likely to die but with tender loving care and dignity. We had to refer him to the palliative care team.

I watched his frail body on the bed, at the same time fighting back my tears, but the tears had refused to stop. As I went to the get some tissues to wipe my tears, the doctors tapped my shoulder. "You need a break." He told me to go now; that I should speak to the nurse in charge to take over my patient on my behalf. I went straight to the nurse in charge to let her know that I would be out of the ward for a short break. I was not in the mood to eat even though it was well past lunchtime. I thought about what we saw on the television about the Chinese and Italian hospitals and COVID-19, and now England is in the same predicament. When would this stop? The number of deaths was increasing every day. I went into prayer. The staff room was totally empty, so I had the liberty to pour my heart out to God amid my tears. I prayed for strength to carry on, prayed for my colleagues, the patients and especially Mr ZE's family.

Back to the ward, I was told that another patient, Mr AY, was due for intubation. Intubation is the process of inserting a tube, called an endotracheal tube, through the mouth and then into the airway. This is done so that a patient can be placed on a ventilator to assist with breathing during anaesthesia, sedation or severe illness. The tube is then connected to the ventilator, which pushes air into the lungs to deliver a breath to the patient (Whitlock, 2020). Intubation is done when a patient cannot maintain their airway, cannot breathe on their own without assistance, or both (Whitlock, 2020).

Although the patient was not directly allocated to me, we worked as a team to support each other. The gentleman was so unwell and extremely breathless. However, the doctor and nurses were exploring all options to help him, hence the decision for him to be intubated. All the patients in that bay were all for TLC (Tender Loving Care). No one knew how long they have as we cannot play God. Who knows—some may pull through.

The was a particular patient, whose wife had developed the fear of contracting the virus, decided to put on full PPE and sat by her dying husband. I ask the charge nurse why she is allowed in but was told that she was a retired nurse from the hospital. I am not sure how clever her decision was, but this is a ward on which all the patients had coronavirus, and all were on a very high percentage of oxygen, as well as nebulizers. As I watched her sitting there, I could only imagine the fear, the pain, the emotional turmoil and sense of loneliness that her husband's death will bring to her and has evoked her to put herself at such risk—to sit by her husband in the last few hours of his life. Standing in the middle of that bay, in my own wonderland, I was asked to transfer the gentleman to another ward with a side room. The idea was for continuous tender loving care and dignity.

On arrival to that ward, I could not in my wildest dreams have thought that such wards still existed in 2020 NHS hospitals. The ward was really old, though covered with paint, but it was very obvious that the ward was in dire need of refurbishment. A ward like that is difficult to keep clean and free from infection; it's risky and unsafe especially with the pandemic. There is no amount of cleaning that would do any justice to the ward other than total refurbishment. The ward is an open massive ward with rows of beds on each side facing each other and a few side rooms. The patients, as usual in most COVID-19 beds, had oxygen masks on. I wondered what would be going on in their minds. They looked as though they were on death sentence. I tried smiling as I made eye contact with them but, of course, my face was covered with a mask and protective goggles. So, I waved at them as I walked by, and my heart ached as I thought of the anxiety, fear, pain and uncertainty thrown upon them by COVID-19. I wish I could tell them that they will be alright, that it is a matter of time.

For me, the one and only thing that kept me going was that God is and will always be in control, no matter what.

CHAPTER 13

PEACE AT LAST; NO MORE PAIN

PEACE AT LAST; NO MORE PAIN

I heard the call bell ringing while I was attending to a patient in one of the bays. As it has been ringing for a while, I hurried up with the lady that I was assisting in order to answer the call bell. This is important because the patient could be in trouble. It was from Mr JJ, the gentleman in one of the side rooms. Mr JJ was a middle-aged man with a history of abdominal cancer. His cancer had been well managed by the oncology team, and he had had a few admissions. He had been stable for the last two years after surgery and things seemed to be working in his favour. He had been admitted this time around because he was infected by coronavirus.

Before the onset of the infection of the virus, he was self-caring, living with his wife and children and back on his job, which he said he enjoyed. He had been transferred from ICU to the ward after six weeks in ICU. He was then unable to mobilise, unable to eat a normal diet except for a few spoons of pureed diet and had a nasogastric feed to meet his nutritional needs. He had been calling for an assistant to use the toilet. He was an unbelievably brave man and despite his problems and the new onset of his disabilities, he managed with an assistant to use the toilet to empty his bowel and pass urine. This morning, it was handed over that it is no longer safe for him to get out of bed as he is becoming weaker.

SURVIVED CANCER BUT DIED OF CORONAVIRUS

That morning Mr JJ was breathless and was on high-flow oxygen. His abdomen was distended, his ankles were oedematous, and we were unable to cannulate him. The team of doctors had seen him, and he was no longer for resuscitation. He had been catheterised and incontinent of faeces. Mr JJ was now a different man, but the only thing that hadn't changed was his smile, which was like his trademark. He had smiled as soon as he saw me come into the room to answer the call bell—he needed help to sip his water. He had been using his call bell more frequently of late.

Sometimes all he was calling for was just to see a nurse in his room. He once told me that he was scared that something really bad might happen to him. I did assure him that the team will visit him as frequently as possible. This was also communicated to the team and included in his care plan. The plan was to visit him as close to every half an hour as possible, just to reassure him. I personally think that he was afraid of dying. He had also told me that his family had kept him going during his tough time with cancer. He had said that if he can survive cancer, he is sure to survive coronavirus. I had to call for help to turn him and relieve his back pain. During lunchtime, the doctor had told me to stop every observation; that Mr JJ was no longer suitable for any medical intervention but to be made comfortable and pain-free. The nurses were quiet as we all knew what would come next, but we did not know when. At 1930, just before the end of the shift, I noticed that the smile was disappearing from his face, his breathing was worse than the last time I went to see him. The doctor had been in constant communication with his wife, and I had also spoken to her. The next morning at about 0955 hours, Mr JJ stopped breathing; the doctor pronounced him dead and stated the cause of death as coronavirus-related complications. We all knew that he was at high risk of the virus due to his history of cancer.

Mr JJ has told us about his Son HZ, who lived abroad and would have like to come and see him in the hospital but for the lockdown. I have heard and seen the father and son chat on Facetime. A few minutes after his JJ passing, the son called for an update. I told him that I couldn't speak to him about his father, but that he needed to communicate with his mother. He was very furious and wanted to speak to his father. I told him that his dad was sleeping and would be sleeping for a long time. He did not seem to understand, he asked me to wake him up but, again, I said that I do not wake people that are sleeping. As he continued to plead with me, I told him to call back in fifteen minutes. He agreed to that and as soon he dropped the phone, I called Mrs JJ, the young man's mother. I told her about the conversation I had with her son. I told her to call her son immediately and update him about on the current situation.

I waited until the end of the shift on hearing from HZ, as I am sure that his mother would have broken the news of his father's death to him. I am not the best at announcing bad news. I must acknowledge my weakness, as I would always hand this chore over to the doctors or the charge nurses to take care of.

During the last conversation I had with Mrs JJ, she was very upset. She noted that her husband had survived cancer but died of coronavirus. Though she was extremely upset, the team had prepared her well ahead of her husband's death.

Mr JJ's fears had disappeared as he lay there on his death bed. I could remember his lovely smile as the words 'Thank you, nurse' seemed to slip from his lips effortlessly. Today he is at peace—no more pain and no more fear—he is left in the room alone with a sheet covering his face as he slept on. Good night, Mr JJ.

WHY ARE PEOPLE WITH CANCER AT A HIGHER RISK OF COVID?

Research has shown that people with cancer who contract the new coronavirus appear to have a greater risk of severe COVID-19 illness and death, but this may depend on their cancer stage and the type of treatment they are receiving. In fact, those with early-stage cancer may fare as well as people who have not had cancer.

Some types of cancer such as lymphoma and leukaemia can affect the immune system (https:www.macmillan.org.uk/coronavirus). Immunotherapy and chemotherapy may also affect the immune system. Chemotherapy and radiotherapy, which are common weapons in the fight against cancer, can also affect the bone marrow and reduce its ability to produce enough white blood cells for the immune system to function properly (Cancer Research Centre UK). Coronavirus is a viral infection that attacks the lungs, so people with lung cancer have a higher risk of the disease. Although I did a lot of research on this subject, I have chosen to keep it simple, as some of the studies need further investigation.

These findings are vital as I had a few instances of nursing patients with COVID-19 with history of cancer. I also have patients and friends whose loved ones have a history of cancer and some whose loved ones had died during this pandemic after contacting COVID-19. It is obvious that I cannot learn everything that I need to know about every condition that puts an individual at risk of COVID-19 in one day, but I promised myself I'd learn as I go along. So, I had taken my days off to do some studies on it although from my nursing experience I already had some idea.

However, I find it necessary to find out more, as COVID-19 is a new disease and the knowledge on it is still limited. A friend of mine had once told me that her brother was asked not to be quarantined due to certain conditions that put him at a higher risk for COVID-19. He was furious, as no one had told him the reason why that condition had put him at a higher risk. I think if people know the reason why they are asked to do certain things, they are more likely to comply. Some of them have told me that the coronavirus situation is about controlling people, which I personally know better. But the only way to answer the question from a professional point of view is by evidence.

CHAPTER 14

"I WOKE UP TO FIND MYSELF IN A MIXED-SEX BAY"

"I WOKE UP TO FIND MYSELF IN A MIXED-SEX BAY"

It was a Friday, and on getting to the ward where I was booked to work, I found it was closed. I also noticed that it was empty. It is not unusual to move or close a ward—this could be due to two wards merging due to reduced use of resources or to sprint clean a ward. I went to the site manager's office and was told where the new ward had moved to. On arrival to the ward, the nurse in charge said there was no PPE. She directed me to a staff room where I waited for two hours with some medical students who were also waiting for PPE. The nurse in charge was particularly kind as she came to apologize for keeping us waiting for such a long time, but she wanted to tell us that the PPE had finally been delivered.

Once with the patients, we came to realise why we had to wait for all the PPE needed. The patients were very unwell, some were intubated, some on high-flow oxygen and some on back-to-back nebulizers. The ward was a mixed bay; this is the third time that I had come across mixed-sex bays since this pandemic. Is it because most of the patients are very unwell? Yet there were two patients among them who were very much alert. One of them, Ms GZ, told me that she woke up two nights ago to find herself in a bay full of men. The other lady in the bay, Mama GF, bless her, would be transferred to the side room as she was dying. I wondered if her family was aware that she was being nursed in a mixed-sex bay. Mama GF's family had phoned me to update them about their mum. However, they had not asked for anything relating to the bay. I asked the nurse in charge if the family was aware of the bed situation. She had told me that she didn't know since she had only come back after four weeks of sick leave after being infected by the virus.

The other lady, Miss LK, was alert and had been given the option to put up a report if she wanted to, at a later date when she got better. But for now, she was still very unwell and on high-flow oxygen. The nurse in charge had told me that she would be moving as soon as there was a bed. She appeared really anxious. We had contacted the family so they could speak to her. Obviously, her family was not happy about her being in a mixed-sex bay, but they were relieved that she was improving and would be looking forward to seeing her at home as soon as possible.

As I remembered it, I knew that a mixed-sex bay is kind of a breach of contract. On the other hand, could it be just that the hospital cannot afford to manage their patients by providing them with a single-sex bay in this pandemic? It is a compliance issue—the Department of Health requires all providers of NHS-Funded Care to confirm that they are compliant with the National definition 'to eliminate mixed-sex accommodations except where it is in the overall best interest of the patient or reflects the patient's choice.' The declarations were to be made on or before 1st April 2011. Organisations that either did not make a declaration or declare that they were compliant would face penalties.
(https://www.dh.gov.uk/en/Publicationsandstatistics/letter-sandcirculation/Dearcoleagueletters/DH__124252).

GOV.UK Eliminating Mixed Sex Accommodation (2011)-Declaration exercise
https://www/gov.uk/government/publications/elimination-mixed-sex-accomodation-declaration-excercise

I guess these accommodations must be due to the circumstances of the moment. Since nobody expected COVID-19 in this magnitude hence there was no way to plan for it. *At the end of the day, safety comes first*, I said to myself. As nurses, in circumstances like this, it becomes our responsibility to maintain the patients' dignity and privacy as well as reassure them in order to reduce their distress and anxiety.

Sleeping in the room or bay with people of the opposite sex is upsetting for some, creating anxiety and undue stress, and often when the patients are at their most vulnerable (Roberts, 2010).

Oliver agrees with the above, even adding that it is threatening. However, his question was: 'Is it worse to be admitted to a mixed-sex bay than to face delay to an operation, be stranded in an overcrowded Accident and Emergency Department for hours, be denied access to specialist clinical areas, or be moved repeatedly between the wards?' He continued by stating that 'Sometimes we simply have to make pragmatic decisions in the broader interest' and finally that 'A universal service for the many will have occasions when the few won't have what ought to be their reasonable expectation met.' (Oliver 2018).

CHAPTER 15

ONE OF THE NURSES DIED OF COVID-19

ONE OF THE NURSES DIED OF COVID-19

The day was hectic and as stressful as ever—some things never change. I was grateful that the shift was nearly over even though there was still a lot to do, including the hundred and one duplicated documentations. At this time of the evening, all the nurses are on their toes tying up all the loose ends of their job and getting ready to hand over to the night nurses.

One of the night nurses arrived really early. We weren't particularly surprised because she has always come to work well ahead of time. I had overheard one of the nurses asking her if everything was alright with her, as she appeared so quiet. She told her that all was well, that she was a bit tired. I thought that it was due to the strain and stress from the night shift that was affecting her.

Just after the handover, I saw two nurses walking quickly to the ward storeroom. I did not show any particular interest because there wasn't anything unusual about it. But then this was followed by an unusual noise. One of the nurses was saying, no, no, nooooo. Apparently one of the nurses who worked in that ward had died of COVID-19; the nurse who arrived at work early had heard the news before coming to work and that was why she had been upset. She had now broken the news to her other friends in the storeroom, hence the noise. The news quickly spread through the ward like a wildfire.

I had worked with the deceased for more than four long days, and that was how I met the nurse. She had been nursing for a while, but she hadn't been employed in that ward for very long. She had called in sick the week before; her close friends knew that she was taken to an intensive care unit, but as far as the ward manager knew she was off sick and ought to be coming back to work the following night. She died that afternoon. The ward manager had called her husband to confirm what she heard.

The ward was now filled with nurses from the day and night staff. Tears were flowing like streams from people's eyes. Everyone wanted to get the full story about her illness up to the point of her death and her social circumstance. It was a fearful and shocking news. Her husband did not pick up the phone but had called back. We waited while the matron was on the phone with the deceased's husband. We were looking at each other, wondering why we had decided to put ourselves in this position. "She has three young children," one of the nurses said. Although we did try to keep it secret from the patients, one of the patients had somehow overheard the news on her way back from the ladies. She had told the other patients in the bay. There was just an unbelievable sadness in the ward.

One hour after we had finished the shift, we were still with the ward manager, trying to get information and asking questions. The ward manager was not sure if there would be enough staff members on duty the following day. She was definitely heartbroken and at the same time trying to organise the rota. She's got to remove the deceased from the rota and look for a replacement. She couldn't ask any of the nurses if they were able to cover the shift as that might seem insensitive. That is the role of the manager; at the end of the day, she still had a ward full of COVID-19 patients to cover. She had to put her managerial skill into action and to arrange for more nurses for the day shift in case any of her nurses were not able to make it due to the effect of the death of their colleague. The nurses had made calls to their other colleagues at home who had not heard the news. The manager had asked the nurses to come into her office so that they could close the door, as they did not want to distress their patients with the noise—some of them were too unwell to be disturbed while others were sleeping already.

The matron had been able to get the full story from the deceased's husband. After she became unwell, the nurse was admitted to her local hospital. She was transferred to ICU, intubated and put on the ventilator. She died two days later. That information was hard to swallow. Why are healthcare professionals dying? What are we doing so wrong? The rate of death is too high, especially among the ethnic minority groups and, even more, the black nurses.

THE CASUALTIES IN ANY WAR ARE THOSE
ON THE WAR-FRONT

The truth is that the true face of NHS is the ethnic minority. What has been shown on the television, in most cases, is not the true representation of the NHS staff. I only see the true representatives on the television when a nurse/care professionals dies. This is because most of them are from an ethnic minority. We all know that the casualties in any war are from the soldiers on the warfront. The true front line in the NHS hospital wards and nursing homes are from the ethnic minority groups. The result of the research that has been done as to why ethnic minorities are dying, in my view, is not far-fetched. The answers are what they are.

COVID-19 patients in NHS hospitals are nursed by mainly ethnic minorities, who are working themselves so hard. They're tired and stressed as well as underpaid. The same group of people had to keep coming back for overtime and for more shifts to make both ends meet. I'm not implying that it is the same for all those NHS care professionals who, unfortunately, passed away throughout this pandemic. If we think about those that are at risk, those that are immuno-compromised, what is the link between stress and immunity? Nurses who are caring for very sick patients as well as being bombarded with endless paper works have no time for a break and may not do well with COVID-19.

Nurses are at risk of burnout; this is characterised by both physical and psychological symptoms—typically fatigue, exhaustion, headache, gut disturbances, sleeplessness, dyspnoea and the inability to fight off minor infection (McConnell, 1982).

In addition to the above, burnout is a syndrome that results from chronic stress at work, with several consequences to workers' wellbeing. In the systematic review of prospective studies by Salvagioni et al., they found out that burnout was a significant predictor of the following physical consequences: Hypercholesterolemia, type 2 diabetes, coronary heart disease, hospitalization due to cardiovascular disorder, musculoskeletal pain, changes in pain experience, prolong fatigue, headaches, gastrointestinal issues, respiratory problems, severe injuries and mortality below the age of 45 years. The psychological effects that were found were insomnia, depressive symptoms, use of psychotropic and antidepressant medications, hospitalization for mental disorder and psychological ill-health symptoms, job dissatisfaction, absenteeism and new disability pension (Salvagioni et al., 2017).

If the above is true and burnout can affect the ability to fight off minor infections, how much chance do health care professionals who find themselves in this situation have? Health care professionals, especially nurses and carers, need to learn how to look after themselves. A nurse can measure, weigh and document patient's inputs and outputs but will forget to use the loo, forget to drink water and not take time to eat. Nurses are with the blood pressure machines all day, reporting the abnormalities to the doctors, while their readings are through the roof. Who cares for their carers?

Usually, nurses are allowed to take their one-hour break during their lunchtime in order to have time to eat and relax before going back to the ward. One of the things that bothers me is that some wards had decided that the one-hour break should be split into two—half an hour each. When a nurse takes a half-hour break, by the time they get to the canteen or warm up their food after queuing for the microwave, half their time is gone. The nurse now has fifteen minutes to eat and queue to use the toilet because there is only one staff toilet in most hospital wards and sometimes two wards has to share one toilet. As if that is not enough, the doctor or any other staff can come to the room to ask the nurse about their patient, medical note or drug chart, or any other inquiry that might warrant the nurse to leave the break room or go back to work. It is not guaranteed that the nurse will take the remaining half hour due to the pressure of work.

Black nurses will be the last group of people to seek the service of a psychologist or counsellor to address certain life or work-related issues. No matter how difficult their working environments are, black nurses are most unlikely to seek help for their physical and mental wellbeing. Times are changing and we need to do things differently; to look after ourselves if we want to enjoy the profession we love.

As I sat on that nursing station that night in my own mental wonderland, I saw my phone flashing. The message was from my daughter Chi-Chi, and she had come to pick me up. She asked about my day as usual, and I disclosed the bad news to her. I had begged her not to tell any member of our family about it as my safety would become of greater concern to them. "Will you be going back to work?" she asked. "You know it's Friday and I do not work on weekends," I replied. "I know you don't, but after the weekend—Monday and onwards?" she asked. "Please give me time to process the whole thing because the news is so heart-breaking," I asked her. I knew she was increasingly worried about me. She held my hand, telling me how she goes home every day after dropping me off at work, to cry out and pray – scared for my safety – and she would often call her boyfriend so they both can pray for me. I held her hand and we prayed for God to give her peace and faith to trust Him that he is watching over me. We then prayed for the health care professionals and the family who had just lost their mother, sister, wife and daughter. It is a hard time, but God is in control, I reassured her.

CHAPTER 16

"YOUR FACE IS THE FIRST FACE I HAVE SEEN FOR OVER A MONTH"

"YOUR FACE IS THE FIRST FACE I HAVE SEEN FOR OVER A MONTH"

It was a Friday, and my best working day of the week. Like most people, I liked this time of the week; not because I don't like my job but because I get to spend the weekend with my family—do some shopping, cooking and, before the lockdown, go to church. I really do not mind finishing late from work or working hard on Fridays. To crown it all, I like to stay up late on Fridays, watch night movies with a glass of Rose on the side. This is because I can stay in bed late on Saturday morning.

Back in this same ward, in which I had been booked for a few times during the last two weeks, I had been allocated to the same bay. Two patients out of the six had been there for a while and I had nursed them before. They were transferred from the ICU. From the handover, it was revealed that one of them would be discharged on that particular day, but it depended on if his wife was happy to take him. The patient in question was Mr DD; he was obviously not completely well, but well enough to go home. The first time I met this gentleman, he was on 60% oxygen, and that is the highest level of oxygen. The amount of oxygen was reduced so much that eventually he was on just 24%. He was being discharged with home oxygen as he was before his admission—that is, back to his baseline.

But DD cannot leave the ward until his wife can take him. "It's not my wife's fault, Esther," he said. "She doesn't want to catch coronavirus. She is very scared because she does not want what happened to me to happen to her." He told me how his family members thought he was losing the battle. He said he was in ICU for two weeks, and after he left the ICU, he couldn't walk. "She does not want to go through the same thing." He told me that she was sorting out the spare room and his oxygen equipment. He told me that they had been married for thirty-five years, and although they didn't have children, they have had each other. While we were still talking, the occupational therapist and the physiotherapist came in to assist DD with mobility. They had also told him that his home oxygen had been arranged through the pharmacist and it was in their spare room. He was happy for all this because the whole discharge planning and input didn't require his effort. The only problem now for the team was that his wife had refused to take him.

She had called the team and told them that she was exposed to COVID-19 through her husband but was never been tested. She had self-isolated, coupled with the lockdown. She told the team that she was at risk because she has a history of breast cancer, though she was cleared. However, she didn't want to take the risk of bringing him home until he had been swabbed for the second time. I had checked Mr DD's record. Although he was swabbed on admission, which was about 4 -5 weeks before, it was not certain that he was cleared of COVID-19. As a new disease, no one was sure if someone who had it once might contract it again. Another point is that the virus that drops on surfaces could be on his clothes and his other gadgets such as his phone and iPad. Based on her concerns, we had asked the doctor if we could take another COVID-19 swab.

The team assisted Mr DD in cleaning his phone and iPad, and he had a shower and got rid of his clothes, including his shoes. His wife will to bring him a fresh set of clothes which a member of the would   pick up from the hospital entrance. I had to give him some face masks to take home. Mrs DD told us that she had another toilet that her husband could use when he came home. With everything in place, Mr DD was set to go home and to isolate himself from his wife while the doctor waited for the result of the COVID-19 swabs. The doctor would have to call Mr DD and his wife to tell them the result of the test. The team with Mr and Mrs DD were happy with the plan.

I was on my break when I heard the team clapping, bidding Mr DD farewell. I wasn't going to miss it, so I quickly left my food and ran out of the staff room. Mr DD was sitting on the hospital wheelchair and being wheeled out by the porter. I ran in front of them, standing right there, I took off my face mask, the goggles and my facial shield and said to Mr DD, "Sir I am

Esther, your nurse." Oh, to my wildest surprise he just broke down. "What have I done, sir?" I asked, thinking that I was in trouble. He said, "Your face is the first face that I've seen for over one month since my admission." That was an emotional moment for him, for the team and myself. This is just one drop in the ocean of the suffering and trials in the ward caused by this enemy of mankind called COVID-19.

CHAPTER 17

INSIDE THE PPE THERE IS A HUMAN WITH NEEDS

INSIDE THE PPE THERE IS
A HUMAN WITH NEEDS

I t was a Thursday morning, and on my arrival at the hospital entrance, I was led by a security man to get my scrubs. When I got there, there were men and women lined up, issuing scrubs according to individual sizes. I thought that was quite cool. Since the history of my care with COVID-19 patients, I have never been in an environment where the staff was designated to assist one with scrubs. I was then directed to another area where I was assisted with full PPE, as another group of staff assisted us with the actual putting on of the PPE. After donning the mask, we were assisted with the testing of the mask to see if we were properly protected. Then we went over to another staff member who wrote down our names.

Woah! I'm really impressed, I said to myself. I was directed to the ward that I was assigned to. Not long after that, I needed to empty my bladder, but I was told that I had PPE. *Hmmmm, what was that supposed to mean?* It meant I had to remove everything and start all over again. The nurse in charge said that I should hold it until my break. This was at 0900 hours. I went back to my patient, suppressing my bladder as much as I could. All the toilets in the ward were sealed, and all the staff had to go out of the ward to use the toilet when they needed to. At about 1100 hours I went back to the same nurse in charge, telling her that I needed to use the toilet. But I was told that there was no one to look after my patient. I had been aware since I was a student nurse that nurses are not allowed to leave the ward without handing the responsibility of their patients to another nurse. These are some of the safety measures that are in place to keep patients in the ward safe. It was 1100 hours and the last time I emptied my bladder was at home at 0530, which was followed by a hot cup of coffee before leaving home. I went back to the patient, feeling even worse. I was doing one-to-one care, so there was nothing to distract me from my anguish—it was a nightmare.

The nurse in charge promised to come to me as soon as she got someone to cover the patient so that I could empty my bladder while on my break. It reminded me of labour pain, when every minute is like an hour. I had checked the clock several times, and each time I checked, it was only two minutes or so passed the last time I checked. At about 1230, the nurse came to me and said, "Oh yes, you are the nurse that was getting burst of urine, aren't you?" I said I was, and she told me to take a break.

The queue and the protocol for removing the PPE were as long as they were for putting them on. As there is nothing without an end, I was finally free to use the ladies' washroom, and I was so grateful that I was in the washroom at last. I couldn't have placed any value on anything other than the washroom at that moment. Free at last, except for lower abdominal pain, it was nothing compared to what I went through. I decided that I was going to only take half a cup of water in order to keep my bladder empty. The break went by so quickly, and I had wasted about 15 minutes undoing my PPE. When I got to the restaurant, I realized I needed another 15 minutes to put on the PPE back on and get to the ward. I had to shove the food in my mouth as quickly as possible to be on time.

After I got back to the ward, I started having stomach upset. The pain in my lower abdomen was also increasing. I knew that it was nature calling, it was time for number 1 and number 2. I couldn't believe what was happening to me. What was I going to do? I tried bearing it, but it was so painful. I went to speak to the nurse in charge, but she was not in the ward. The other nurses were too busy to even look at me. The nurse that was my close body had a patient who was very unwell, so it meant that she couldn't leave her patient for even one second. She had told me earlier that she too wanted to use the washroom but there was no one to relieve her. "Esther," she said, "I feel so sick." That told me that I was not the only one feeling that way and I should learn to hold it as long as it takes; after a while, one's body gets the message—it gets used to not going to the washroom as soon as you should.

I went back to my patient, praying to God to help me. After a while, my abdomen appeared to settle down a bit as I continued to do my work. The urge was coming off and on until I started having pain in my lower back. I was leaning on every piece of furniture that was on my way. I couldn't sit down but I could lean on the tables and cabinets around me. All the doors in the bays were closed and no one was allowed to open the door and go from one bay to another. These measures are for infection control, so the nurse in charge could be in one of the bays. The abdominal pain had eased, and I was left with just back pain. I continued the shift until it was handover time.

The shift was finished and there I was again, in the same ladies' washroom—this time it took longer because it was a double act. I was going home, so I did not care how long that visit was going to take me. The pain in my back was so bad that I felt like taking a taxi home, but there was none. I eventually got on the wrong bus, and then I realised I couldn't even sit down because the pain on my back was too terrible. I decided to wait until I got to any train station, it didn't matter which. The journey home took me twice as long as normal, but I was grateful that I took the train. I wanted to cancel my shift for the following day, but it was too late; the agency might not get a replacement. If there is anything that I hate, it's for a nurse to book and agree to a shift and then cancel. It just puts a lot of pressure on the team that's already overwhelmed with work. I decided that I would go to bed and that when I woke up in the morning, I would call the agency if the pain is still there. Funny enough, that night I slept like a baby.

The following day while at work, my agency consultant called me to ask me about the shift. I told him that it was okay, but he told me that he would never send me there again because he had heard too many complaints about the hospital and the PPE. He said, "Esther, I know you don't like to complain, but I am not going to send you there anymore." *Woah, I have not spoken to anybody about my ordeal, what caused him to make that decision?* I knew God was and is on my side and watching over me.

SOME HOSPITALS HAVE IT ALL; SOME, JUST ABOUT

Come to think about it, where do we find the balance? Some hospitals had so much PPE and all their procedures are so on point and even excessive. Then you have places that will remind you that you have PPE on so you cannot go out again and have to wait for your break. And remember, after dressing up, the individual's name is taken down—this is to control the usage of PPE. They need to control their stock so you really cannot blame them. My issue is that we as humans will always answer the call of nature. Nature does not understand the scarcity of PPE. Behind the PPE is a human who has human needs.

On the other side of the coin, there are some hospitals at which you get into the ward and are told that they have no scrubs, or scrubs have not been delivered and you need to go to ICU or XXX ward to get scrubs. When you get there, it's not guaranteed that there will be someone to go to look for scrubs for you that morning because everyone is busy. You may need to go around to a few wards to find scrubs. The masks used in the ward comes down to what is available. No one knows whether we are protected or not, as we do not know how the testing was done.

Some wards will tell you to keep your surgical mask the whole day, except when it is wet

Really and truly, this has put a lot of health-care professionals at risk. It is very difficult to blame the hospital because they are all doing their best with what little resources they have, while the government is playing politics with PPE. Everyone that is in touch with the news would have heard all the shambolic problems with the government and the availability of PPE. There are only two reasons why this would be the case—either those in a position to provide the PPE did not understand the implications or they simply did not care. They do not understand what impact their action and their inaction have on people's lives.

CHAPTER 18

THE DAY
I REALISE I'M
GOING TO WRITE THIS BOOK

THE DAY
I REALISE I'M
GOING TO WRITE THIS BOOK

The site manager entered the ward on time to remind every member of the staff that all the patients in the ward were going to be moved out of Ward A to Ward D. Ward A is going to be sprint cleaned when it is emptied and will be used as a COVID-19 free ward. Thank God, the number of COVID-19 patients is reducing. I expressed my feelings to one of my colleagues that this pandemic will come to pass away. She asked me how I was so sure that we would ever see the end of this? I apprised her of my belief that nothing has ever come to stay permanently in this temporal world. As I bent toward her to reassure her, she impatiently exclaimed that she could not wait any longer.

The porters were arriving, and the patients had been told that they will be moving to another ward. The ward would be half full and other patients would be coming to join us from other wards. That means we would be receiving patients from left, right and centre for the rest of the shift. We might have started the ward as COVID-19 free, but before you know it one or two COVID-19 patients will slip their way in. Now we had moved in and settled the patients, and the ward appeared quiet. We were not busy, for a change, so I decided to go round to visit the patients at their bedsides. I noticed that some of them appeared to be in a really low mood. I also noticed that the first patient was upset.

I'M MISSING MY DOG

"Hello," I said to her, "are you okay?" She shook her head. Why?" I asked. "I was told that I will be going home today, but I'm not sure that it's going to happen. Do *you* know?" she asked. I knew that she wasn't going home, but I didn't know where she had gotten her information from. I went to read her note, but there was no discharge date in her care plan. "Ms FL, I know that you desperately want to go home." "Yes," she said, at the same time nodding her head. "Would you like to go home and come back tonight?" I asked. She said, "Nooo," to which I asked, "Why?" "There's no way I'm coming back to this place when I go through that door," she said. "So, you need to get well before you go home, and your home will be there waiting for you. Who is at home?" I asked. "My baby," she said. I asked her who was looking after the baby while she was in the hospital. She told me that she lived by herself. I was utterly astonished.

"You're kidding me!" "She is the best dog in the whole world," she remarked with fervour. *Oh, thank God. It is a dog!* I asked her who was taking care of her dog in her absence. She told me that her neighbour was taking care of her; he takes her on a walk and also feeds her. "All right, she will be fine then. How long have you been in the hospital?" I asked her. She replied that she had been hospitalized for over six weeks. "Hmmmm," I exclaimed, "that's a long time, but all will be well."

She suddenly began to tell me about her dog, and I noticed that each time she called the dog's name, she smiled. I asked her to tell me what it was about the dog that made her smile. "She is so cunning and mischievous. She is like me," and this time she was laughing out loud. "What breed is she?" I asked, and she replied that she was a mixed breed, mongrel, brown and white colour, and 'she really likes her food and sometimes she steals mine. She is called Gasper'.

The whole conversation was becoming interesting and, if nothing else, it was making both of us laugh. So, I told my FL that I would be writing a book and I wanted to write about the relationship between Gasper and her. I quickly went to my handbag and grabbed my notepad and began to write. That was my first inspiration—to get into the minds of post-COVID-19 people to find out about their feelings during this pandemic.

She spent a long time telling me about her and Gasper while I wrote. She showed me a picture of the dog, which was tattooed on her arm. Then she scrolled through her phone with her magnifying glass and showed me their pictures taken in different places, including a dog show. "Where is it now?" I asked her how often they go out for a walk. "We only go out when my neighbour is free to go with us," she said.

I asked why, and she replied that it was because she is partially blind. "Oh, OK. Sorry, I didn't know about this as I have just met you," I said.

The ward hostess brought Ms FL a cup of tea, and I assisted her in positioning her table to avoid an accident. After gaining this wonderful rapport with her, I then went on to ask her if she would agree to tell me about her experience with COVID-19 in hospital. "Nurse – no, Esther I said (sitting up on her bed) – I thought I had the flu but before I knew it, my body was boiling at the same time I was shivering. My dog looked so sad and wouldn't eat. I came to hospital only when my dog was barking nonstop. My neighbour, to whom I'd given my key, opened the door and let himself in and found me. I slept on the chair for two days unable to eat and drink and was covered in my s--- and urine when he called the ambulance to pick me up.

"If not for my dog barking, I would have been dead by now," she went on. "So many things happened to me which I cannot remember. As a partially blind person, you don't know where you are; you lean on other people to direct you and explain to you where you are. That was the situation I was in—unable to speak, on oxygen, and the only thing that kept me going was the thought of my dog. I lost my mum and sister to the pandemic; two weeks before I became ill, they both died. My sister was asthmatic, and mum died in the home where she lived. No one was allowed to see them, though I am partially blind, I would have loved to hold my sister and tell her that I loved her and say goodbye. I have other things wrong with me, so my sister used to come and cook for me, but now I am not sure of what is going to happen to me when I go home because I am weaker than ever.

"Before I came to the hospital, I walked the dog with my neighbour, did a few house chores, washed my dog and washed myself. I kept my house clean and spotless. My neighbour does my shopping on Friday evenings because he owns his little business in the local market.

I was in ICU—look at my arms and my neck they are still panful." I looked at where she was touching, she would have had Venflon and PICC line put in at the ICU.

"I was fed from my nose and had all kinds of machines connected. Everyone had been nice to me, but the best thing that happened to me is you being able to sit by me and talk to me. If nothing else, I can talk about my dog. People are not even aware that I am partially blind," she said. So, I offered that I was sorry for her troubles but maybe people didn't know of these because she was doing so well. I had checked her record and there was nowhere that it was documented that she was partially blind. I should add it to the note and let the doctors know and update their notes. She went on to say, "The physiotherapist tried to walk me with the zimma frame, but I was scared that I would fall if I used a walker." "Why did you not tell them that you are partially blind?" I asked. "I didn't because that was how Mum ended up in the home. Blindness is in our family, but my sister does not have it. She was asthmatic instead. Nurse, do you know that I now have to wear a pad all the time now? I call for help but before I know it, I am already dirty or the bed is wet. I'm only 35 years old. The coughing was horrible; it felt as if my bones and ribs were going to crack. I ached so much, and my whole body was so weak that I had to learn to sit down again. Then I was transferred to Ward A. It's a hard job for you nurses and I don't think I could do what you do for any amount of money in the world," she thankfully acknowledged my efforts.

"If it is your passion and you've had the right training, you can," I replied. She returned to her recounting. "I hated the oxygen masks and was so happy when I could breathe without them. I also hated being fed from my nose— it's like, what is all that about? I took it out three times until I was able to eat again normally. Thank God for that."

The pain in her expression was evident when she was narrating this to me. The truth is that I was only able to sit down and talk to her because the ward was half full. Nurses would like to sit down and chat with patients, but it is almost impossible. Not because of the patient's needs but due to the the unnecessary duplication of documentation. We spend more time on these papers than we spend on the patients themselves. Most nurses really and truly want to know about the patient and have a relationship with them. After all, many have considered the nurse/patient relationship as the core of nursing and it is described as a 'dynamic lived reality characterized by a sense of spiritual connection, which is an experienced bond of energy' (Halldorsdottir, 2008).

As I left Ms FL's bedside, intending to keep my notepad in my handbag, I noticed that Mrs MG appeared to be very moody. I did smile at her under the face mask but, unfortunately, she couldn't see it.

HOW IS MY HUSBAND GOING TO MANAGE AT HOME?

So, I went to her and said, "Hello, Mrs MG, my name is Esther. Unfortunately, you cannot see my face, but I've got on a very beautiful red lipstick." Oh, my God, she laughed so hard and so did the other patients in the bay as they overheard me. The idea was just to find a way of breaking into her world. "Can I offer you a hot drink?" I asked. Who says no to lovely hot drinks? Now everyone on the bay wanted some hot drink, so I had to take their orders, including orders for biscuits and cakes. Again, remember that I had no patients, so it was easy to meet such requirements. As the patients settled down with their cups of tea/coffee and biscuit/cake, I went back to Mrs MG, saying, "So, Mrs MG, how are you today?" She replied, "I must tell you, nurse, before you came, I just wanted to run away from this place but the only thing keeping me here was that I cannot even get out of this b------ bed, let alone leave the ward. That is frustrating the living H--- out of me." I told her that I intended to write a book and I wanted to record our conversation in my diary. She smiled with her eyes wild open—MG had the loveliest blues eyes. "Why do you want to leave the ward?" I asked her. She expressed her frustration in reply, "Because I am fed up. I just want to go out there and do what I used to do before. I used to work under the council cleaning schools. I used to like to keep the place clean and make sure that when the children come to school, everywhere, including the classrooms, was clean. Now I am being told that I cannot do it anymore. And what about my garden?" she wondered, "Who is going to look after it for me?"

"Who is at home," I asked, "My Husband," she replied. "Okay, that is good. Is he well and able?" I asked. "Yes," she replied. "Mrs MG," I offered, "you know that your body has been through a lot—from ICU till when you were transferred to the ward due to coronavirus. It is only fair that you allow your body time to heal itself." "How is this going to happen?" she asked. I told her that it would be possible through rest, good nutrition, and as much exercise as she could tolerate while making sure she complied with medical advice. I further told her that she might still be able to go back to work or do something easier than she had been doing in the past. I suggested to her that she might help her husband in gardening. However, she euphemistically remarked, "Oh no, he is useless." We both laughed. "Okay I hear you loud enough to understand what you mean," I said, "but at least he can wheel you to the garden and you can tell him what to do; both of you walking together will make a difference." She was still but appeared to be staring at me. "Are you okay?" I asked. "Yes, just thinking, that is so true," she said. As I now had her talking, I began to ask her about her experience as a COVID-19 patient.

She told me how she has a sensation on her throat, and in the evening, she noticed that she was warm and she was shaking. Her husband had called 111, who advised that she should take paracetamol. About 0100 hours the following morning she could not breathe so her husband called the ambulance. She told me that until that day she had never been on a hospital bed and had no reason to be as her husband and herself had no children. She told me that she spent four weeks in the ICU. She recollected, "The nurses and doctors were nice to me but were frightening; they all had their faces covered with big face masks. I had tubes all over. I was too breathless and weak to do anything. After four weeks in the ICU, I couldn't even get out of bed, I am just beginning to sit up by myself. Life just changed suddenly, and I have not set my eye on my husband ever since I fell ill. We do talk, but he is not into the modern phone," she said, "so we can only speak. Esther, do you know what it is not to be able to know when you have to go and depend on other people to clean you up? Sometimes you are too embarrassed to call for help, and you even feel guilty troubling the poor nurses who already have too much to do. But you have to call for help because it does smell, and you cannot hide it anymore. Even that, it is easier in the hospital—how is my husband going to manage at home? One minute he has a wife who is a professional cleaner, and the next he has a stranger that wets herself and messes up his bed."

"Things do get better," I reassured her, "as you work with the physiotherapist; you build up your muscles and you will be in control." And again, she continued with anguish. "Another thing is the pressure sores from the ICU. I have always slept on my back, and now I have to lay on one side or the other, which is uncomfortable."

"MG, you just have to keep lying side to side and eventually the sores will be healed," I reassured her. She kept on. "The food, nurse. Please do not get me wrong. The portions are small, and the food is tasteless, but then again it is free, and I am grateful that I can eat orally. I know that everyone is so kind, but I would like to go home soonest." Unfortunately, the discussion was interrupted by the physiotherapist who had come to assist Mrs GG in standing. "Well! Mrs GG, the physiotherapist is here; thank you for your time," I said in parting tone. "No," she said, "I should be thanking you."

SHE IS AT RISK OF ABSCONDING

As soon as I left Mrs GG, I went straight to my bay to find out if there was any admissions, but there was none, and it was nearly lunchtime. The nurse in charge had handed me a piece of paper with a list of names on it. The list contained the names of my patients and the ward where they were coming from. "There is one particular patient that you have to be careful with," she said. "She is suicidal and at risk of absconding. She came in with an overdose and goes out to smoke every half an hour. She is a nightmare."

She had told me to keep an eye on this patient as she is one of those who end up getting nurses in trouble. I felt that those were unfair and harsh comments about someone we never met before, and I was determined to give this patient a fair chance—not be judgemental but to be kind and accept her for who she is, while at the same time mindful that she is at risk of escaping.

"Please make sure she has an escort with her at all times when she is out to smoke," the nurse in charge continued, "Normally she would have a mental health nurse, but that has been discontinued. You and your health care assistant should be able to manage," she said. "How and why did they stop the registered mental health nurse?" I asked, "I have no idea" she replied. Every nurse in the ward had helped with serving the meal and as soon as the lunch was finished, there came my first patient, then the second, the third and the fourth, all in a matter of fifteen minutes. The last patient that was transferred was my patient who was at risk of absconding and overdose (Miss KG). As she walked into the ward, I introduced myself to her and showed her to her bed, proceeding to take the handover from the transfer nurse.

Just before the handover was completed, KG told me that she was going out to smoke. I asked her to wait for me by her bedside. I went to her bedside after the handover. I took some vital signs and quickly took some details from her. I brought her some water and offered her a cup of tea. I asked her to follow me while I showed her around the ward and introduced her to the team. I also introduced her to the other patients in the bay. We both had kind of quickly built a rapport, and from then on, I knew that she was not as bad as she was portrayed to be. At the end of the assessment, she told me again that she wanted to go out to smoke. I told the Health care assistant to escort her out to the smoking areas. The health care assistant refused, saying that smoking is against her religious beliefs. I had to remind her that she was not in the ward as a result of her religious beliefs but for patient care. The patient herself did not want to be escorted, and she told me that she did not like people following and watching her all the time. So, I had to speak kindly to her and mention that if she goes out by herself, I might lose my job. She had quickly accepted being escorted out by the HCA, and I asked her to be quick and to take care of herself. "Yes, I will nurse," she had replied.

She doesn't look or sound anything like the handover that I got from the transfer nurse, I said to myself. I have learnt to treat people with an open mind, and not to act on other people's experience, but to experience something myself before taking action. KG had come back earlier than expected. I went back to her to complete my assessment. I brought her a cup of tea with milk and two sugar, and she was very happy that I brought her a cup of tea without her asking. Moreover, I remembered how she liked her tea. I thought this was the right time to ask about her as she might talk about why she had decided to commit suicide. The assessment was really going well until she suddenly stopped talking and started to wipe her eyes. "What is the matter?" I asked, "Did you want to go out to smoke?" "Yes actually, I could do with a stick of cigarettes." I told the nurse in charge that I was going for my break. I told her that I will use the opportunity to follow Miss KG out for a cigarette. "Oh Esther, I would never guess you smoke," the nurse in charge said. "Oh yes, I do. Only five sticks a day," I replied. I have never smoked in my life, but I just wanted to go out with Miss KG to see if there was anything that she had to tell me off the record.

On our way out, I told her about myself and my family. I also told her about my job and hobbies, my intention to write a book and my decision to start writing and why. She also told me about herself and how she had just lost her fiancé to COVID-19. "As there seems to be no life for me anymore, it was easier to finish it all," she said. "The dream wedding and all our plans to start a life together were thrown out of the window."

"I'm so sorry this happened to you—another horrible encounter," I stuttered, as I wasn't expecting this. I went silent but nodded my head. "When the ambulance came, I was disappointed that my attempt had failed," she said. "Who called the Ambulance?" I asked. "My flatmate, bless her, she had no idea what it was. I think the ambulance crew would have found the evidence. My family was almost destroyed when the hospital called them. My flatmates were confused, and they had no clue what to do. One of them had my sister's mobile number because they chatted together all the time, but she forgot she even had the number."

"Would you attempt such a thing again?" I asked. "No, never ever, no way." "Good," I said. She told me that she will be going to live with her family when she is discharged from the hospital. We walked back to the ward slowly. She was very grateful; she told me that, apart from the psychiatrist, I was the only one outside her family that she had mentioned the reason for her action. "People are too judgemental and treat one based on their present circumstances. I am labelled as a suicidal patient. I hear them talk to each other. I am treated as someone who deserves what she got, just because I sort of inconvenienced them by going out to smoke. I am telling you this because you told me you have the intention of writing. A nurse called me, 'that wicked patient'. I have never known what it is to be wicked, but ZO and I have always loved people. COVID-19 took him from me in the blink of an eye. I was not allowed to see him. The only visit I had was in the mortuary." She was now shaking as she sobbed. I didn't want to ask any further questions as I wasn't willing to start that something that we might not be able to control.

After we went back to the ward, she sat by her bedside watching a film on her iPad. She had no further trouble and had not asked to go out to smoke cigarettes. The only complaint she had was that she was served the wrong meal. I apologized and ordered her sandwiches. My next encounter with her was when I went to tell her good night at the end of the shift. "Thank you again," she said.

As I work through the ward, I pondered about what I had heard from these three patients. One thing I knew for sure that they had in common was uncertainty, fear and anxiety about the future. Ms FL did not know what to do after she has lost her mum and sister to COVID-19, as her sister would usually come and cook for her. To make things worse, her eyesight was getting worse and she was immobile. Definitely, she will get help from social service, but she is scared and anxious about what the future holds for her. Could that be the reason why her dog means so much to her? COVID-19 has taken a lot from her and she is left with Gasper. The story of her affiliation changed my perspective about things. I have to look at the world with a new lens. If someone approached me in the past to pray for their dog, I wouldn't think about doing it because my time is too precious for that nonsense. However, the truth is that we may never understand how things that don't make sense to us can mean the whole world to others. Their lives could depend on those things, and no matter how trivial or how insignificant it may seem to us, that might be one reason that person still clings to life. This will stay with me as long as I live.

Mrs MG was also worried about the unknown! She was anxious about losing her dignity, mobility, independence and the job she loves. Her job might not be the greatest in the minds of some, but she took pride in what she does, happy to see the children study in a clean learning environment. As the saying goes, one man's meat is another man's poison. She feels that COVID-19 had taken away the thing she liked to do; even the garden that she felt pride in making beautiful will no longer get her attention.

Miss KG is no different! Although we can all pass judgement on what she could have, and would have, and should have done, until one is in someone else's shoes, they will never know why someone does what they do. All her plans were so perfect in her mind – her perfect wedding and her perfect home – only for her dreams to be tarnished by COVID-19 in front of her eyes!!! How will she begin again? How can her life be rebuilt? The energy and the time she had spent falling in love to the point of being engaged was now a waste, and there was no other way out but to end it all.

Though the time it will take these patients to rebuild their lives is unknown, it is achievable with a lot of support. That was the night I decided to tell the story from my own point of view. I can now settle down and write, as COVID-19 is on the decline in London, United Kingdom.

THE EFFECT ON STRESS ON NURSES

We knew that the ward was going to be busy, but nothing had prepared us for what happened that late afternoon. We had all sorts of patients with multiple complex issues. We had patients with infectious diseases, psychiatric patients that were fighting us and at risk of absconding, and we had patients with bleeding wounds but not allowing a dressing to be applied. Now we are talking about the serious risk of infection to the nurses and other patients.

We had confused patients who needed all care, including feeding, and were at risk of falls. Patients' families were calling to find out about their loved ones. Some had called more than three times within a short space of time, especially those with large families. During this pandemic, when patient's families are not allowed to visit their loved ones, you cannot blame anyone for wanting to call several times a day, as they are anxious. We have been encouraged to exercise patience whenever patients' families are inquiring or when they demand to speak to nurses and doctors. Families want to know what their loved one had for breakfast, lunch and dinner; they want to know about their weight and when they were last weighed; they want to know the hospital's next plan of action for their patient; they want to know about medications, why their loved one is on it and when their antibiotic or fluid is stopped or is going to be stopped, etc. These bits of information are vital to them. Sometimes the nurse has to go back and forth to get this information. It is not always easy for the nurses, who have a thousand and one things to do at one time. It is equally hard for anxious families. It is bad enough to have a loved one in hospital, but to have someone there during this pandemic is a different ball game. My own workload was so heavy that I had to protest, and the other nurses, including the nurse in charge, had no choice but to come to my aid.

THE NURSE IN CHARGE WAS CRYING

The time went by so quickly while we were still trying to complete the paper works. The nurse in charge was handing over but somehow it had taken a long time and nurses were becoming impatient; they were tired and wanted to go home. After the handover, we heard someone crying somewhere in the ward. We instantly thought that the cry was from a patient. The nurses were all over trying to find out which patient was crying. It didn't take long for us to find out that the cry was from the clinical room. That room is always locked, so it was obvious that the cry was from a nurse. We quickly rushed into the room, only to find a nurse crying; that was serious because she was the nurse in charge of the night. She was so upset that she could not speak.

We later found out that it was the state of the ward that was making her cry. It will be easier for an outsider to judge her action, but it appeared as if she had become overwhelmed with the whole thing. She was a very young nurse, had patients of her own to look after, then she was also in charge of the whole ward. If any of those patients who are at risk of absconding absconds, she would be supporting the nurses to deal with the police, family and paperwork, as well as having to explain to her superiors. The complexity of her responsibilities, including staff and patient safety and wellbeing, overstretched her abilities and the pressure had built up inside. She was probably afraid that if things weren't well-managed, she would be in trouble. We had to call the site manager, who came to speak to her to find a way of helping her manage the situation. Although the day nurses desperately wanted to go home, our priority had now changed. It was no longer about us going home or any of our self-centeredness— it was about the mental state of our fellow nurse, our comrade and sister in the profession. My feet seemed to be glued to the floor until I saw my phone flashing. My daughter had given me ten minutes to meet her in the car park as she had been waiting for 20 minutes already. While I was reading her message, the site manager asked us to go home. On my way home I prayed for God's strength and His peace to cover the young charged nurse.

THE IMPLICATION OF STRESS ON NURSES
AND PATIENT CARE

We were asked to go home because everything was under control while the site manager was there. However, the problem didn't end there, and it is still what it is. Nothing had changed in terms of the patient's needs. At the end of the day, the site manager had his role and his job description, part of which, I guess, would be to support the nurses but not to sit in a particular ward the whole night. Why exactly should a nurse be in charge and still have her own patients? It isn't that there were no nurses to do the work; there were a lot of agency nurses who were not working due to the current low demand for agency nurses at that moment. It's all about cost-cutting, which could put both patients and nurses at risk as patient's care is would be compromised. The nurses and the nurse in charge end up being overwhelmed with work and stress, anxiety and burnout. Think about it—what happens when a nurse is stressed? What is the association between stress and performance?

Stress is a natural feeling of not being able to cope with specific demands and events (Felman, (2020). Even nurses themselves often don't see anything wrong with living in constantly stressful situations. We get used to it, and it has become part of us to the point that if we are not stressed, it's as if there is something wrong. Nurses see it as not perform-ing; we are immune to the effects of constantly being in stressful situations. Even when we have completed our daily tasks with patients for that day, our job is only starting. It is not unusual for a nurse to leave the ward two hours extra after a very stressful day and come back to work on schedule the following morning. I know that, in order to perform, we need some level of stress. I get that. But to some extent, there's a point where the level of performance will be reduced. This is also supported by the Yerkes-Dodson law concerning the em-pirical relationship between arousal and performance. This law dictates that performance increases with physiological or mental arousal, but only up to a point, as when the level of arousal becomes too high, performance decreases. (Yerkes and Dodson, 1908).

Have we sat down to wonder why nurses sometimes make the mistakes that looked silly? Or why nurses are underperform-ing? If this is not convincing enough, let's look at the effect of stress on our health. Stress can become a chronic condition if not well managed, and the demand could be from multiple sources such as work, financial pressure, etc. Although stress is essential for survival through the fight or flight mechanism, when there are too many stressors at one time this can be harmful to both physical and mental wellbeing. This is due to an increased release of chemicals such as cortisol, epinephrine and norepinephrine. This in effect increases the individual's blood pressure, sweating, alertness and muscle palpitation. In addition to the above, epinephrine and norepinephrine cause a faster heart rate. Physical stress can increase blood pressure and respiratory rates, slow down the digestive system, decrease immune activity, increase body tenseness and cause sleeplessness due to a heightened state of alertness (Felman, 2020).

Prolonged stress can lead to chronic stress, and that, if not kept under control, can lead to cardiovascular, respiratory, quality of sleep, immune system and reproductive problems, as well as diabetes, depression, anxiety and a decline in mental health. These are the kinds of risks that nurses put themselves through daily to earn a living (Felman,2020).

I can hear you saying what a carry on. I had to carry on because of the implications of stress on nursing care and the nurses themselves. It's surprising that nurses care for their patients but are seriously damaging their own health. It is not uncommon to see posters of NHS promotion on health and wellbeing, but how can the health and wellbeing of staff improve if they are working under constant stress? Are those posters there to tick the boxes, or is the system truly concerned about promoting the health and wellness of their staff? Really, they cannot be doing a good job of promoting health care if their doctors and staff are constantly being put under undue stress. In 2020, with all the modern technology, it is unfair for nursing staff to still be working under such levels of stress. If nurses are valued the way the public thinks of them and the way they're being portrayed as heroes during the pandemic, the public must advocate on their behalf.

CHAPTER 19

ARE COVID–19 PATIENTS READY
TO FACE THE WORLD?

ARE COVID-19 PATIENTS READY
TO FACE THE WORLD?

After the handover from the nurse in charge and induction of the ward, I was finally introduced to my patient, Mr ZV. He was not particularly happy with another nurse being introduced to him, because he'd become tired of seeing different nurses. I thought that was strange—how did he expect just one nurse to look after him all the time? During the handover, I was told that he is at risk of fall, hence he is on one-to-one nursing care. I was told that I needed to make sure he does not fall out of bed. I thought to myself that if a young man of forty-five years has to be taken care of to prevent him from falling out of bed, it must mean there is something wrong. I had to go back and read his note.

The gentleman had been infected by COVID-19, and he had a history of diabetes and asthma, with cognitive impairment. He was in ICU for six weeks, where he was intubated and put on a ventilator; now he had been in the hospital for eight weeks and was unable to get out of bed. It was handed over that he had to sit up out of bed because he needs to go home. At that moment he was all care but was able to feed himself. After he had his breakfast and some personal care, I decided to get him out of bed. He had refused to sit out. I had spoken to the nurse in charge, but she had told me that he must get out of bed as he was being prepared to go home. The nurse in charge told me that ZV doesn't want to leave the ward, but he has to go home as he has been in hospital for a long time. I went to the patient to encourage him to get out of bed, and he later agreed that he would try with the available aid. I managed to sit him up on the side of the bed with his feet on the ground. I then noticed that he was sweating profusely. I had just taken his vital signs and blood sugar; both were within a safe range.

After two attempts, I decided to involve the physiotherapists. The two of them had been working with him and had planned that the nurses should have him sit out on the chair daily. The physiotherapist might have been sitting him out at other times, but not the nurses. As the therapist came to sit him out, we noticed that he continued to be overly sweaty, and each time they tried to get him up he would fall back to bed. I suggested to the doctor that he must be anxious. What is he anxious about? She had written him up for some medication to help cope with his anxiety. Using medication to help with anxiety is only a temporal measure and not a cure, I said to myself. We have to accept that the fear and anxiety for COVID-19 patients are real, especially with their uncertainty of how to move on after the trauma to their physical and mental wellbeing caused by the infection.

DIABETES AND COVID-19

There are 3.9 million people who have been diagnosed with diabetes in the UK, according to the statistics 2018-2019. One in ten over 40 now have type 2 diabetes (www. diabetes.org.uk/ statistics). Diabetes has been a special concern since the outbreak of coronavirus in China. Research has established that people with diabetes are at a higher risk of dying from COVID-19. Diabetes is a risk factor for hospitalisation and mortality of the COVID-19 infection, and the virus is a double challenge for patients with diabetes. (Madsbad, 2020).

In comparing intensive care and non-intensive care patients with COVID-19, there appears to be a twofold increase in the incidence of patients in intensive care with diabetes (Del Rio and Malani, 2020). Mortality seemed to be threefold in people with diabetes compared with the general morbidity of COVID-19 in China (Yang and Yu, 2020).

WHY IS THIS GROUP OF PEOPLE SO SUSCEPTIBLE TO CORONAVIRUS?

Diabetic patients have an impaired immune response to infection, both concerning cytokine profiles and changes in the immune response to infections, including T-cells and macrophage activation (Ferlita et al., 2019). It has also been well documented that patients with poor glycaemic control are at risk for infections. This is also supported by Critchley, who states that poor glycaemic control is powerfully associated with serious infections and should be a high priority (Critchley, 2018). Madsbad stated that the problems caused by loss of glycaemic control make treatment difficult for patients with underlying factors such as fever, poor food intake and the use of certain drugs in patients with respiratory treatment (Madsbad, 2020).

Several studies, such as Hutten and Syrjanen (2013), Honce, R. (2019), Almond, MH, Edward, M.R. et al. (2013), state that most type 2 diabetes patients are obese, and without a doubt, obesity is a risk factor for infection.

Further to the above, late diabetic complications such as diabetic kidney diseases and ischaemic heart disease may complicate the situation for people with diabetes, making them frailer and further increasing the severity of COVID-19 disease and the need for care such as acute dialysis (Madsbad, (2020).

REHABILITATION

At that point, I started thinking about everything that COVID-19 survivors go through. There must be some element of fear and anxiety about how they can move on with their normal lives and protect their loved ones. Has this been dealt with by the government and our health care system? Is there any advice from the World Health Organisation for the world at large on this? Although there are some tips out there about how to cope, what about those in hospitals who are recovering, especially those that have been in ICU for a long period? Most people in this group are too traumatised to research coping mechanisms.

The government prediction is that:

> Up to 45% of post-COVID-19 patients will need some form of low level of medical or social input for recovery.

> 4% will require more focus, on an on-going, intense rehabilitation in bedded setting.

> 1% will find that discharge planning is not an option.

(https//:www.assetspublishingu.serviceuk/government/ upload/ystem/upload/attachment_data/file/874213/COVID-19_hospital_discharge).

The NHS discharge to assess model (Covid-19 Hospital requirement 19 march 2020)
assumed that:

> Fifty percent will require no imput from health and social care.

> Forty-five percent will need support from health and social care.

> Four percent will require rehabilitation in bedded setting.

> One percent will find that discharge from the acute bed is not an option.

Rehabilitation is a set of interventions needed when a person is experiencing or is likely to experience limitations in everyday functioning due to aging or health conditions, including chronic disease or disorder, injury or trauma (https://www.who.int/ new-room/fact-sheet).

Early rehabilitation in ICU may reduce physical and mental health complications frequently occurring in survivors of critical care, among which COVID-19 survivors are not excluded (Parker and Srichaaroendchai 2013).

Mr. ZV was in the intensive care unit for a long time and was still in an acute bed, with cognitive impairment, lost mobility, and inconsistent of urine and faeces. I wondered if psychological input was incorporated into this recovery plan before or alongside discharge planning. If it had been done, would it have made a difference? Certainly, I understand that resources are stretched, but if a certain aspect of care is not dealt with at the preliminary stage, it will become a big issue at a later stage.

A failure to identify, diagnose and treat this functional problems, disabilities and cognitive impairments in individual with co-morbidities following ITU is worrying (Murray-et al 2020) The significant post-acute/ICU care needs of COVID-19 patient rehabilitation will significantly result in a reduction in acute capacity, poor long-term patient outcome and higher associated health care utilisation, and create greater challenges further along the line (Murray et al., 2020). There is a saying that goes: "A stitch on time saves nine."

In my view, some of these COVID-19 survivors could do well with a psychologist while they are still in hospital. On the other hand, there could be a sort of facility, much like the rehabilitation centres for COVID-19, for post-acute and ICU patients. This would enable them to get all the necessary therapies from the multidisciplinary teams to prepare them to go to their home or their residence. A comprehensive plan must be made for the 50% of COVID-19 patients who will require some form of on-going care following admission to intensive care, to improve their long-term outcome and free up much needed acute hospital capacity (Murray et al, 2020). There should be planning in place to create post-acute care resources and facilities for the high number of people with physical, psychological and functional trauma of prolonged intensive stay and hospital admission following COVID-19 (Murray et al., 2020).

Plans for rehabilitation programmes in different settings, in my opinion, should also include some sort of support for families that may not have experienced COVID-19 themselves but went on the traumatic and heart-wrenching journey with their loved ones who were nursed in acute wards or ICU and had somehow pulled through. These patients are often left with some health challenges as a result of the insult from the pandemic. And last but not least are those families whose loved ones, unfortunately, passed on and left them with psychological trauma, financial hardship, loneliness, shattered dreams and the hopeless situation that comes from having no clue where and how to begin a new life. The world is broken and needs fixing.

I AM GRATEFUL

On my way to work, I reflect that I am grateful that watching and listening to the news the night before about coronavirus and the state of the world is not going to change my appreciative attitude towards life. I need to be grateful even for the little things and count my blessings. I am grateful for the good times and the times that are not so good. Grateful to God for myself and anybody that is breathing today. My experience since this pandemic has made me see life from a different perspective.

On my way to another hospital. although we are still locked down, I owe my gratitude to God for His benevolence and mercy. This is not because I am immune to the problems of the world today. In January, my niece died due to haemorrhage after a Caesarean section. She was survived by my elder sister (who is her mother), her husband and four children, among whom was a one-day-old baby on the day of her death. Three months prior to that, we lost another niece of mine due to an asthma attack.

My three grandchildren are all living with their parents. Two from one parent and one from another parents are all having symptoms of COVID-19. They are not eating, having constant diarrhoea and temperatures of 39 and above. I have been communicating with them through the phone and advising their parents since I cannot visit them. We are all praying, we are fasting with the church for forty days and I am part of that—not every day, but on certain days of the week.

Sometimes I have to fast while on a twelve-and-a-half-hour shift. During this extremely hard time one's spiritual antenna is very important.

I appreciate the fact that public transport is running to get key workers to their workplaces. I appreciate my comrades in the profession for their courage and their support for patients and families. I appreciate the fact that we are there to support one another regardless of the difference in our specialties. I personally have decided that I am going to be strong no matter what I have to go through. I am not going to live in fear but will protect myself as well as humanly possible and carry on with my job. I am not going to be overwhelmed by everything going on around me, but I'll find the strength to do my job in the best way possible. I am in it, and I am not going to stop. I have already seen too much during this pandemic to stop. In fact, I truly never liked Mondays after the weekend, and I've always liked to stay home on Mondays for extra rest. I could if I wanted to, and that is the beauty of being an agency nurse—you can work when you want and sometimes where you want. But even though I don't like to work on Mondays, I can still discipline myself to do it. Lately, I am eager to work even on Mondays, as I know that there is someone that needs help.

The sad truth is that some patients will die and no one can do anything about that, but one of our roles as nurses and doctors is to help people get well or better, and, for those that will, unfortunately, die, to die peacefully and with dignity. To be there for them as much as I can while they are taking their last few breaths, as they say goodbye to the world and transit to the other side, when there is no family around them to do so is especially important,

I am grateful for their contribution on this earth during their time.

I THOUGHT I HAD FINISHED WRITING THIS BOOK

My daughter (Chi-Chi) was unusually quiet as we drove through the black-walled tunnel from the South East of London towards East. "Why are you so quiet, girl?" I asked. I knew she had been quiet all day, but I thought it was work-related, so I was happy that she was going to have some rest the next day, Saturday. Then I noticed that she was tearful, "What on earth is happening to you to the point of you shedding tears on the steering wheel?" "Someone close to me has lost her dad," she said. "That's sad. Where and how? Here in London?" I asked. "To coronavirus," she said. I thought to myself, I am exhausted now; there is nothing more to say, as I have said it all. I have nursed patients, consoled and counselled families, prayed and fasted along with my church – as we prayed for families, friends, NHS, the government, and even for the entire world – because of coronavirus. I have shaved my hair to keep my family and myself safe, given my finances to support family members, friends and strangers, to feed them due to their hardship during this unprecedented time.

I have also taken it to another level by writing this book, using intensive literature research to get evidence-based information on the coronavirus. And here I am—my daughter has lost her friend's father, I am speechless, and so I have to go back to my writing desk and write once more. My daughter's friend's dad is called Mr PP; he was an extremely successful businessman and a true father to his children. He has sent his children to the United Kingdom to study. He came to visit them in the UK just before the lockdown, but before he could go back to his home country, since most countries were locked down, he of course found he couldn't travel back. While in the UK he contacted the virus and was admitted into one of the NHS hospitals, where he died. I hope my daughter and her friends will read this book and understand the pain in my heart and the trauma I have been through when I remember my precious comrade who died in the battlefield, the fear and anxiety my patients and their families had to deal with, and the patients who took their last breath on my shift, some with me by their bedside, holding their hands.

Finally, may I seize this golden opportunity to say thanks to all those doctors and nurses who had to put their lives at risk to nurse and care for all the patients during this pandemic. To all the health care workers, all NHS workers, carers in the nursing homes and communities, our spiritual leaders who prayed and fasted for us, all the frontline workers, and the precious TOUCH team of ICAN Community Church. Thank you for making a difference and being the difference that makes the difference for the world to become a better place.

This will too shall pass, and the rest will be history. We shall come out better, taller, stronger, healthier, wiser, richer, more caring and more loving.

I am indeed grateful.

Esther

REFERENCES

REFERENCES

1) Alhazzani, W., Moller, M.H., Arabi, Y.M., et al.
    (2020). Surviving Sepsis Campaign: Guideline on
    the Management of Critically Ill Adults with Coro
    navirus Disease 2019 (COVID 19). *Intensive Care
    Med.,* 2020, pp.1-34.

2) Barnes, L. et al., (2019). Syringe Driver:
    Standardising Protocol to Minimise Error.
    End of Life Journal, 3:3, pp.43-50.

3) Begley, S. (2020). With Ventilators running
    out, doctors say the machines are overused
    for covid-19. Available at: https://www.statnews.
    com/2020/04/08/doctore-say-ventiltion-
    overused-for-covid-19

4) Cancer Research UK. How can cancer treatment weaken immunity? Available at: www.cancer research/uk.org/about-cancer/cancer-ingeneral/ coronavirus-and-cancer.

5) Centre for Disease Control and Prevention (2019). Coronavirus Disease 2019 – People Who Are at Higher Risk for Severe Illness. Available at: <nb The information was updated by the CDC June 29 2020 to reflect new information and findings.

6) Chen, Q., Zheng, Z., Zheng, C., et al. (2020). Clinical Characteristics of 145 Patients with Coro navirus Disease in Taizhou, Zhejiang China. Available at: <https://www.ncbi.nlm.nih.gov/ pmc/articles/PMC7186187/> [Accessed 28th April 2020].

7) Critchley, J.A., Carey, I.M., Harris, et al. (2018). Glycemic control and risk of infections among people with type 1 or 2 diabetes in a large primary care cohort study. Diabetes Care. 41:21 pp. 27-35.

8) Care Quality Control. Supporting Note. Mixed sex accommodation. (https://www.dh.gov.uk/ en/Publicatinsandstatistics/lettersandcircula tion/Dearcoleagueletters/DH__124252).

9) Dean, E. (2020). Covid 19: Guideline on When to Admit a Patient to Critical Care. Available at: <http://rcni.com/nursing-standard/newsrci. com> [Accessed 28th April 2020].

10) Del Rio, D.C. and Malani, P.N. (2020). Covid-19 – New Insight on a Rapidly Changing Epidemic. JAMA.2020. doi:10.1001/jama.2020.3072.

11) Felman, A. (2020). Why Stress Happens and How to Manage It. Available at:

https://www.medicalnewstoday.com/ articles/145855.

12) Ferlita, S., Yegiazaryan, A., Noori, N. et al. (2019). Type 2 Diabetes Mellitus and Altered Immune System Leading to Susceptibility to Pathogens, Especially *Mycobacterium tuberculosis. Journal Clinical Medicine, Vol.8,* 12 2219.

13) Gilroy, R. (2020). Nurses raise alarm after practice sent PPE with altered expiry date.

Nursing Times, 17 March. Available at: http:// www.nursingtimes.net

14) GOV.UK Eliminating Mixed Sex Accommodation (2011)-Declaration exercise

https://www/gov.uk/government/publications/ elimination-mixed-sex-accomodation-declaration-excercise

15) Halldorsdottir, S. (2018). The Dynamic of Nurse-Patient Relationship: Introduction of a Synthesized Theory from the Patient Perspective. *Scand J. Caring Sci; 2008, 22,* pp. 643-652.

16) HM Government (2020). NHS Covid-19 Discharge Service Requirements. Available at: https//:www. assetspublishingu.serviceuk/government/ upload/ystem/upload/attachment_data/ file/874213/COVID-19_hospital_discharge [Accessed 30th April 2020].

17) The Holy Bible. The King James Version, Second Printing, Hendrickson Publishers Edition (April 2016). China: RR Donnelly. (Deuteronomy 31:6).

18) The Holy Bible, King James Version, Second Printing, Hendrickson Publishers Edition, (April 2016). China: RR Donnelly. (Esther: 2-10).

19) Iyendo, T.O. (2016). Exploring the effect of sound and music on health in hospital settings:

A narrative review. Int J Nurs. Stud 2016, NOV VOL 63, pp. 82-100.

20) Jeffers, S. (2017). *Feel the fear . . . and Do It Anyway.* London: Vermilion.

21) Knight, S. (2008). NLP at Work: *Neurolinguistic Programming, the difference that makes the difference in business, second edition.* London: Nicolas Brealey. pp. 235.

22) Leung J.M., Yang X., Tam T. Shaipanich, et al. (2020). ACE-2 Expression in the Small Airway Epithelia of Smokers and COPD Patients: Implications for COVID-19. *European Respiratory Journal 55:2000688;* DOI:10.1183/13993003. 00688-2020.

23) Madsbad, S., (2020), Covid-19 infection in people with diabetes. Available at: https:// www.touchendoctinology.com/insight/ covid-19-infection-in-people-with-diabtes/.

24) McConnell, E. (1982). *Burnout in the Nursing Profession.* London: Mosby.

25) Miller-Merrell, J. (2019). Benefit of Workplace Transparency. 5:11. Available at: www.glassdoor. com/employees/blo.

26) Mohlenkamp, S. and Thiele, H. (2020). Ventilation of Covid-19 patients in intensive care units. Available at: <http://www.ncbi.nlm.gov/pmc/ article> [Accessed 20th April 2020].

27) Morens, D.M., Daszak, P., Taubenberger, J.K. (2020). Escaping Pandora's Box - Another Novel Coronavirus. *N Engl J. Med. Doi:101056/ NEJMp2002106.*

28) Morgan, S., Evans, N. (2004). A Small Observational Study of the Longevity of Syringe Driver Site in Palliative Care. International Journal of Palliative Nursing. Vol 10, No 8, pp. 405-412.

29) Mukoreka J., Sisay, I. (2015). Safe Practice in Syringe Pump Management. *Nursing times, 111, 14,* pp. 9-21.

30) Murray A., Gerada C., Morris, J. (2020). We Need A Nightingale Model for Rehab After COVID-19. Available at: <https://www.hsj.co.uk/commis sioning/we-need-a-nightingale-model-for-rehab-after-covid-19-/7027335.article> [Accessed 5 July 2020].

31) Mushtaq, B. (2018). Assertiveness in Nursing, SKIMM Nursing College, Srinagar, India. *08:06 2018, Volume 3 Issue 3,* p. 272.

32) National Early Warning Score (NEWS). (2017). Standardising the assessment of acute -illness severity in the NHS. Available at: https://www. rcplondon.ac.uk/project/outputs/national-early-warning-score-news-2

33) National Foundation for Infectious Diseases. (2020). Common Questions and Answers about Covid-19 for Older Adults and People with Chronic Health Conditions. Available at: https://www. nfid.org/infectionous-disease/common-questions-and-answers-about-and-people-with-chronic-health-condition/

34) O'Hare, R. and Wigan, K. (2020). Imperial to Begin First Human Trials of New Covid-19 Vaccine. Available at: https://wwwimperial ac..uk/news/198314imperial -begin-first-human-trial-covid/

35) Oliver, D. (2018). Mixed Sex Wards May Be Inevitable. BMJ 20/10/ 363: k4223, page 105. (BMJ 2018 The ref. is 20 Oct 2019 page 105).

36) Parker, A., Sricharoenchai, T. (2013). Cur Phys Med Rehabil Reports. 12:1(4). pp. 307-314.

37) Phua J., Weng, L., Ling, et al. (2019). Intensive Care Management of Coronavirus Disease 2019 (COVID- 19): Challenges and Recommendations. *Lancet Respiratory Med. 2020* DOI: 10.1016/S2213-2600(20)30162-2.

38) Pink, D. H. (2006). *A Whole New Mind.* New York, Penguin, pp. 159

39) Recovery Trial Statement, 2020. Statement from the Chief Investigator of Randomised Evaluation of Covid-19 Therapy (RECOVERY). Trial on Hydroxychloroquine. Available at: <http://www.recoverytrial.net/files/hcq-recovery-statement-050620-final-002-final-002.pdf> [Accessed 5th June 2020].

40) Roberts, M. (2010). Q&A: Mixed Sex Wards. Available at: <https://www.bbc.co.uk/news/health-10985944

41) Safa, M. et al. (2015). Severity of Anxiety Disorders in Patients with Chronic Obstructive Pulmonary Disease. *Iran J Psychiatry, 10(2)*, pp. 128-132.

42) Salvagioni et al. (2017). Physical, Psychology and Occupational Consequences of Job Burnout: A Systematic Review of Prospective Studies. Available at: <http://www.ncbi.nlm.nih.gov/pmc/articles> [Accessed 30th June 2020].

44) Shi, Y., Yu, X., Zhao, H., Wang, H., Zhao, R., Sheng, J. (2020). Host Susceptibility to Severe COVID-19 and Establishment of Host Risk Score: Finding of 487 Cases Outside Wuhan. *Crit care 2020, 24:108.*

45) Simonnet, A., Chetboun, M., Poissy, J., et al. (2020). High Prevalence of Obesity in Severe Respiratory Syndrome Coronavirus-2 (SARS-Cov-2) Requiring Invasive Mechanical Ventilation. Obesity (Silver Spring). 9th April 2020.

46) Sissons, B. (2020). How Does COVID-19 Affect COPD? Available at: <www.medicalnewstoday.com> [Accessed 12 May 2020].

47) Toru, U., Ayada, G.S, et al. (2015). Serum Level of RAAS Components in COPD. *European Respiratory Journal* pp. 3970; DOI:10.1183/13993003.congree-2015.PA3970.

48) UK Government: Eliminating Mixed Sex Accommodation-Declaration Exercise 2011. Available at: https://www.gov.uk/government/ publication-mixed- sex-accommodation - declaration-exercise

49) Wan, Y. J., Shang, R., Graham, et al. (2020). Receptor Recognition by Novel Coronavirus from Wuhan: An Analysis Based on Decade-long Structural Studies of SARS. *Journal of Virology, 94 (7)*, e00127-20. DOI:10.1128/JVI.00127.

50) Werman, Howard A., Karen, K., Mistovich, J. (2004). Continuous Positive Airway Pressure (CPAP) in Werman, A. Howard, A. & Mistovich, J. *Prehospital Emergency Care.* Karren K (eds) 10e. Pearson Education, Inc.

51) Whitlock, J. (2020). What is intubation and why is it done? Available at: https://www.veryhealth. com/what-is-intubation -and -why-is-it-done-3157102

52) Yang, L.B., Zhao, Y. et al. (2020). Prevalence and impact of cardiovascular metabolic disease Covid-19 in China. *Clinical Research in Cardiology, 109 (5)*, pp. 531-53.

53) Yang X., Yu Y., Xu, J. et al (2020). Clinical Course and Outcomes of Critically Ill Patients with SARS-cov-pneumonia in Wuhan, China: A Single-Centred, Retrospective, Observational Study. *Lancet Respiratory Medicine,* DOI:10.1016/ S2213-2600(20)30079-5.

54) Yerkes, R.M., Dodson, J.D. (1908)."The relation of strength of stimulus to rapidity of habit-formation" Journal of Comparative Neurology and Psychology, 18 (5), pp. 459-482.

55) Zhong, J., Tang, J., Ye, C. (2020) The Immunology of COVID -19: Is Immune Modification an Option for Treatment? *The Lancet Rheumatology.*

Printed in Poland
by Amazon Fulfillment
Poland Sp. z o.o., Wrocław

62245468R00134